SPECIAL UNITS

COMMANDOS

Ilustrations: Octavio Díez Cámara, Acmat, Audiovisuele Dienst koninklijke Marine, Bundesministerium der Verteidigung, Ejército Portugués, Eurocopter, FN HERSTAL, Giat Industries, Korps Commando Troepen, Orcatron, Peter van Bastelaar, SIG, Simrad Optronics, Sirpa Gendarmerle, Steyr and Thomson-CSF.

Production: Ediciones Lema, S.L.
Editorial Director: Josep M. Parramón Homs
Text: Octavio Díez Cámara
Editor: Eva Mª Durán
Coordination: Eduardo Hernández
Layout: Rakel Medina

ISBN 84-95323-42-7

Photocomposition and photomecanics: Filma Print, S.L.
Barcelona (Spain)
Printed in Spain

SPECIAL UNITS

COMMANDOS

THE U.S. SPECIAL FORCES

The U.S Army maintains some military groups, popularly known as the Special Forces, for special missions. These groups consist of specially trained personnel capable of carrying out any type of military or international support mission around the world.

They have a high level of operational success due to their professional qualifications and the technologically advanced equipment they use. This enables small groups of men to organize and carry out very complicated missions. These groups are normally used as military support for their fellow troops or other armies, and they have been highly successful in the most recent conflicts in which they have intervened.

Worldwide missions

The Special Forces are made up

Helicopter transport
Helicopters are used by the Special Forces for a speedy arrival to the area in which they are to operate and an equally speedy departure once they have completed their mission.

of soldiers trained to carry out the following missions: UW (Unconventional Warfare), DA (direct action), SR (Special Reconnaissance), FID (Foreign Internal Defense), CT (Counter Terrorism), PSYOP (Psychological Operations), CA (Civil affairs), HCA (Humanitarian and Civic Action), wartime support, and other special missions.

Operational qualification

The first type, UW, covers those military and paramilitary actions carried out in enemy territory where there is a need for guerrilla warfare techniques such as subversion, evasion and escape, sabotage, and other covert operations. These types of missions tend to be lengthy, and some also rely on the collaboration of local forces that have been specially trained for the task.

DA missions involve the discovery, disarmament and destruction of targets as well as the capture and recovery of personnel and equipment during strategic and operational maneuvers. They are short missions that require specific skills such as the illumination of targets or the use of explosives.

SR actions are initiated by infiltration of reconnaissance troops behind enemy lines to obtain pertinent information about the enemy and his weapons capacity. This includes the localization of targets, information on the damage suffered to these targets after an attack, and the collection of meteorological, hydrographic, geographic and demographic data.

FID operations are designed to assist the military and police forces in ally countries in confronting various kinds of threats or subversions. They also help to train troops and act as support during humanitarian actions.

Anti-terrorist missions require highly specialized skills to protect,

On any terrain
The Green Berets are trained to operate anywhere in the world. However, each of the five groups in action is responsible for a specific area.

deter or combat radical groups.

PSYOP work to influence foreign attitudes so that they are more favorable toward U.S objectives. This involves swaying the opinions of foreign governments and capturing threatening individuals and organizations.

CA operations are established to strengthen relations with civilian or military authorities or so that the civilian population can take charge of military tasks.

CA operations are established to strengthen relations with civilian or military authorities or so that

Personal equipment
The Green Berets stand out from similar troops in other countries for their wide variety of equipment complemented with the most sophisticated armaments.

M4 WEAPONS SYSTEM

The M4 carbine is a version of the XM-177 design used during the Vietnam War. The first batches were purchased from Bushmaster in 1990 just before Desert Storm, and in 1995 another 50,000 units were ordered from Colt Firearms. These weapons, with a .223 Remington cartridge, are derived from the M16A2 assault rifle. They include substantial changes in the rifle butt, which is collapsible, in the barrel, which is shorter and can hold a single-shot grenade launcher, and on the upper part of the control mechanism, which has a transport handle. The handguard is new as a result of the MWS (Modular Weapon System) program and the development of the SERFS (Swam Extended Rigid Frame Sleeve).

The central rail on the upper section can hold a conventional transport handle with rear sight, an AN/PVS-4B night visionl viewfinder and an Aimpoint Comp-M laser point system. It can also integrate a 4x32 Trijicon ACOG (Advanced Combat Optical Gunsight) viewfinder with a self-lighting reticule and a ballistic curve of .223 for distances up to 1,970 feet. The new handguard is made up of an aluminum structure and an exterior framework with a RIS (Rail Interface System) hook on each side to attach spotlights, AN/PAG-18 visible infrared lasers, 40 millimeter M-203 grenade launchers, pistols and even bipods.

the civilian population can take charge of military tasks.

The Special Forces also carry out many other missions including the seizure of intelligence information, support for military communications and weapons systems, medical assistance, and operations entrusted to them by the President or the Defense Secretary. In addition, they develop strategies and doctrines for their own forces and train other similar organizations, organize preparations for special missions carried out by joint commands, design and acquire all the equipment necessary for their operations and supervise the professional development of all the personnel in their charge.

The A Team

Operational Detachment A of

Individualized armaments
The Special Forces have at their disposition a wide collection of weapons systems that have been optimized for maximum performance during each mission. Such is the case of these assault rifles modernized to a M16A3 variant.

the Special Forces, or the A Team, is the essential core of the units of the U.S. Special Forces. They are also known as the Green Berets because of the hats which identify them. Each of these teams is composed of 12 men under the command of a captain. There is also a second officer in command and two NCO (noncommissioned officers) trained in each of the five functional areas: weapons systems, engineering and demolition, medicine, communications and operations and intelligence. In addition, they are all capable of speaking different languages.

The A Team is capable of a variety of activities including planning and leading special missions (whether they be isolated or part of a larger military operation), infiltrating and extracting from zones by land, sea or air and carrying out operations in remote areas or hostile environments for long periods of time with very little external support. They also develop, organize, equip and train local forces for special missions, support other U.S or ally governmental agencies, plan and carry out all assigned

operations and develop other special missions led by higher-ranking authorities.

To carry out infiltration operations, six people on the A Team are trained in deep sea diving techniques and another group of six in parachuting. In general, these groups are outfitted with highly powerful communications equipment including satellite links and high frequency radios, medical units with sterilizing and resuscitation equipment, night vision equipment, materials for all types of demolitions and weapons for defense or perimeter coverage. This equipment is distributed according to the type of mission to be carried out.

Special organization
The organization of these teams is formed as follows: a Company is made up of six teams and a B team in charge of completing tasks for the staff officers, establishing communications and carrying out various support duties. A Battalion consists of three Companies, and a SFG (Special Forces Group) of about 1,400 troops is formed from three Battalions, a Command Company and a Support Company.

At present, the USASOC (U.S Army Special Operations Command), which has its base at Fort Bragg, North Carolina and reports to the USSOCOM (U.S

Fort Bragg
This important base is home to the Green Beret Monument located in front of the U.S. Army John F. Kennedy Special Warfare Center and School.

THE U.S. SPECIAL FORCES

Training

Before leaving for a combat mission, a plan of attack is prepared and executed on home terrain in order to coordinate the movements and function of each soldier.

Special Operations Command) in Florida, maintains five active SFG's composed of troops from the U.S Navy and two more with units from the National Guard. These groups are complemented with other specialized troops made available by the general staff at Ft. Bragg.

The active SFG's are: the 1st Special Forces Group at Fort Lewis Washington, which is responsible for the area from the Far East to the Pacific Ocean and has a battalion stationed on the Japanese base at Okinawa, the 3rd and 7th at Ft. Bragg, which cover Africa and Latin America respectively and the 5th at Fort Campbell Kentucky, which is in charge of the Mid East and normally has forces stationed in Saudi Arabia. The 10th at Fort Carson Colorado maintains one of its battalions at Fort Dewens in Germany from which is covers all of Europe. The 19th and 20th are composed of units from the National Guard in Draper, Utah and Birmingham, Alabama.

The John F. Kennedy Special Warfare Center and School coordinates the activities of all the groups, and it is also the center where the troops receive their initial training and test various types of equipment. In addition, it maintains active the 1st Special Forces Operational Detachment-Delta (SFOD-D) created in 1977 to confront terrorist threats and undertake those delicate missions which require troops at the highest operational level.

Team

The basic deployment unit is called the A Team, a team of twelve men who together possess all the necessary skills to fulfill all types of missions; in addition, each member has a general knowledge of all the subjects.

The training process

The soldiers that make up these units have been submitted to a long and intense process of selection. Those with the best qualifications, who also pass the Special Forces Qualification Course (SFQC), earn that sought after green beret.

The course Q

The SFQC, or Course Q, hones the skills a soldier needs to successfully complete missions for the Special Forces. This includes the knowledge of unconventional tactics and training on how to travel without restrictions in water, desert, jungle, mountains and arctic areas. Successful completion of the course requires excellent physical fitness and a high level of mental endurance.

Course Q is divided into two parts: an initial phase lasting 40 days and a specialized phase of between 24 and 57 weeks.

GLOBAL POSITION SYSTEM

The use of GPS (Global Position Systems) portable equipment, like this model from Rockwell used by the U.S Army, on the modern battlefield has spread. GPS has applications that range from automatic bomb guiding systems for the most precise impact to establishing routes for divers to follow. It is configured by a small module (which grows smaller with every new model) with a visible antenna in the center that receives data from a new system of satellites in stationary flight around the earth. By triangulating the information from three of the satellites, it calculates the exact location of the operator and provides him with coordinates via a display or alphanumeric screen. Its margin of error, which varies with each model, is only a few feet, and with the help of a keyboard, the desired route can be introduced into the system and its movement followed over land, sea or air.

Its cost has been reduced to $1,000 for a military version that is resistant to the bumps and bangs often incurred during combat.

In the first part, which takes place at Camp Rowe, the soldiers must pass three training phases: individual knowledge, MOS (military occupational specialty) qualifications and group training. The course covers ground maneuvers, overcoming obstacles, patrols and small unit tactics. It ends with a personal interview with those in command and a 65 day course that is mandatory before passing to level CMF 18.

Those who pass these requirements and are selected move on to specialized training in 5 different MOS's. The training covers theoretical and practical knowledge relative to the duties the sergeants will be responsible for on the A Team: command, armaments, engineering, health or communications.

The commander of the detachment (level 18A-SF) follows a 24 week course at Ft. Bragg to develop the planning and leadership skills which will enable him to

Climbing up a wall
A soldier in the 1st Battalion of the 10th Special Forces Group, with its base in Germany, listens to the explanation of his instructor on how to climb up a wall using only his hands and feet. The harness and cord are safety elements used during the exercise.

supervise the actions of the other members of the group. The weapons operator (18B-SF) trains for 24 weeks in tactical knowledge, the use of weapons to destroy armored vehicles, the use of all types of U.S and foreign arms, indirect operational support, portable anti-air defense systems, weapons positioning and developing an integrated and coordinated firing plan.

Those who choose the engineering specialty (18C-SF) spend 24 weeks learning their assigned duties: battleground fortifications, use of explosives for sabotage or demolition and the construction of buildings and bridges. Health matters are entrusted to a sergeant (18D-SF) who has trained for 57 weeks in areas such as advanced medical procedures, treating all types of traumas, surgery and dental and veterinary procedures. He will also carry out missions of support for the civilian population.

The communications specialist (18E-SF) trains for 32 weeks in

Program for the future
The U.S. Army is already working on improving combat conditions, which implies the use of more deadly equipment and a greater capacity for global actions.

various spots including Ft. Bragg and Camp Bullis in Texas. He also follows an 8 week course in AIMC (Advanced International Morse Code). This phase teaches him to install equipment and antennas for high frequency communication, transmit radio waves and other communications procedures and techniques. The course ends with an exercise in which he must demonstrate his ability to communicate with any place in the world.

All the sergeants must pass a final phase of 38 days of classes in air operations, preparation for direct actions etc. and culminating with the Robin Sage Field Training Exercise. The officers, who have already undergone a lengthy and continuous training period at West Point and other institutions, must also pass an advanced course called the IOAC (Infantry Officer Advanced Course); those who posses specialty knowledge of armor-plated vehicles take the AOAC. They must also learn other languages and be provided with in-depth information of the areas in which they might be deployed.

Proven capacity

The first modern example of the U.S. Special Forces is found in the 1st Special Service Force formed in July 1942 with troops from the United States and Canada and initially trained at Fort William Henry Harrison in Montana. The operational success this unit enjoyed during World War II led to the creation, in June 1952, of the 10th Special Forces Group, located

Light troops
Because of their qualifications, operational tactics and ability to function in any situation, these types of special troops may be qualified as light, although they are highly effective in comparison with the rest of the armed forces.

Constant preparation
One of the things that makes these units special is that members are constantly training to maintain their personal skills and learn all the techniques related to their specialty.

at Ft. Bragg under the command of Colonel Aaron Bank. This was followed by the formation of the U.S Army Special Warfare School in 1956, the 5th SFG in September 1961 and the 8th, 6th and 3rd in 1963. President Kennedy officially recognized the SFG's with his visit to Ft. Bragg in 1961.

The conflict in Vietnam brought these troops to Asia in June 1956 when the 16 units of the 14th Special Forces Operational Detachment arrived. Their activi-

ties at Nam Dong, Lang Vei, Dak To, Song Zoai and Plei Mei were well-known, and they received many medals and decorations. At around the same period, special forces were also deployed in Bolivia, Colombia, Guatemala, the Dominican Republic and Venezuela; one of their missions was the search and capture of the Cuban leader Che Guevara.

The end of the Vietnam War also brought an end to three of the groups, and the others were reassigned to various places around the world. In 1989 they participated in Operation Just Cause during which they invaded Panama, and in 1991 they intervened in Operation Desert Storm. More recently, they have been deployed in Albania, Bosnia and Somalia.

They are also sent to the most remote parts of the planet on all types of military and special operations.

Missions in a conventional war as well as those in special situations require the deployment of qualified men capable of using various models of high precision rifles to obtain the most accurate impacts. The operators of these sophisticated weapons systems are normally high-ranking soldiers, and their targets tend to be missile launchers or surveillance radar. Some soldiers are also recommended for the job by their superiors because of their special skills or courage.

High economic returns

Teams of high precision marksmen can carry out a wide range of missions, which is very profitable from the point of view of cost efficiency. These missions become more and more varied as more sophisticated weapons appear that can fire a range of munitions depending on the requirements of military forces.

A marksman's training

During the special instruction that soldiers follow to become commandos it is already evident which men are the most qualified to be select marksmen, either because of their innate qualities or prior training.

Those assigned to the task must also be in excellent physical condi-

Day or night

Modern precisions rifles are equipped with viewfinders that allow for highly accurate shots during the day and optronic modules for nighe use.

tion to be able to move without restrictions over any type of terrain, have some knowledge of parachuting and diving in order to infiltrate enemy territory, and be able to survive in an environment which is generally hostile to their presence.

Training in the use of high precision weapons includes both theoretical and practical subjects. The theoretical material includes how to conceal oneself using the natural environment, how to optimize a shot by calculating peripheral distances or other factors and how to adjust the aiming device and adapt it for nighttime use. Soldiers also learn

Tactical necessity
Marksmen in the Dutch Special Forces are deployed with camouflage uniforms in order to hide themselves and their weapons. This allows them to find the most suitable location from which to neutralize a variety of targets.

about the maintenance of the various mechanical elements of the model to be used and general information on how and why to use the different kinds of munitions.

Tactical preparation ranges from practice on firing ranges with fixed distances of 100, 200, 300 and 500 meters to deployment by various means including helicopters and four-wheel-drive motorcycles. Soldiers are also submitted to qualification tests in different areas such as snowy mountains and water so that they become familiar with the influence of temperature and moisture on the final result of a shot. They also participate in exercises against targets located at positive or negative angles or at distances that are larger than normal. This training prepares them to tackle any situation that

might arise during the deployment or operation.

Adaptation of materials
The resources available to the special units of different armies depend on various conditions ranging from the politics of a certain

government to participation in real operations that put an army's capacity to the test.

Normally small armies or those from countries with restricted funds resort to the use of different types of standard assault rifles, weapons that are generally capable of reaching distances up to 100 feet. Among the more sophisticated models are the Swiss SIG550 5.56 mm manufactured by SIG and the Israeli Galil Sniper produced by TAAS.

Military forces also use derivations of civilian products that have been adapted to be more resistant and

Complete camouflage
High precision marksmen, known worldwide as snipers, use camouflage to blend into their environment and hide their presence from the enemy.

reliable for military use. These models stand out for their low cost and possibilities for use, and many of them have been developed based on the Remington 700 bolt action rifle, which joins the heavy barrel to the ergonomic butt to obtain the best results possible from the rifle. Also economical and with a wide variety of uses are those rifles derived from the 7.62x51 mm (.308 Winchester) M1/M14 series. They are semiautomatic, easy to use and are often sold at bargain prices from the arsenals of those countries that have thousands in reserve. The same features are held by the Soviet Dragunov and similar models manufactured by nations that had bonds with the former USSR.

More sophisticated weapons are produced by the German firm Heckler und Koch, which designs derivations of the 7.62 mm G3 assault rifle adapted to be used as a high precision weapon. Among these semiautomatic models is the SG/1 with improvements such as a bipod and an attachment for a viewfinder, the MSG90 with a long 24 inch barrel and a butt that can be

BAFFLER

High precision shooting not only requires hitting targets from large distances, but also the action of shooting must be discreet as the marksman must rapidly fire off several shots before abandoning his hiding place. Consequently, an element is usually placed on the muffle of the rifle barrel to reduce the explosion associated with firing. It has several chambers or holes to vent the gas.

It is very simple to use, and some models can be separated from the weapon to attach a silencer. It also reduces the recoil that affects the marksman's shoulder as a result of the detonation of gunpowder from the munitions.

It is normally made of steel so as to resist the harshness of combat, and its shape varies widely according to manufacturer. Some are cylindrical with many holes, while others have to big side vents.

The most powerful
The Barrett M82A1 is very powerful and easy to operate so it can be fired three or four times in a row in less than ten seconds. It is powerful enough to destroy a wide variety of targets including armored command vehicles

adapted to the user, and the PSG-1 whose high price makes it unavailable to countries with lower purchasing power.

Other excellent offers include the SSG69 from the Austrian company Steyr, the TRG manufactured by the Finnish firm Sako, the French FT-F2, the German Mauser and the Swiss SSG2000/3000.

Weapons to satisfy all requirements

The market offers a wide variety of high precision rifles –both bolt action and semiautomatic. Developed from assault rifles or hunting rifles, what sets them apart is their price (generally connected to the accuracy of the shot) and their caliber, which determines the maximum range and the success of impact against various types of targets.

The Accuracy series

Great Britain is home to the headquarters of Accuracy International, a company that is enjoying a great amount of success with its high precision bolt action rifles. These rifles have been sold to countries such as Germany, Australia, Canada, Spain, the United States, Italy, Oman, Sweden and to Britain's own armed forces.

These weapons, which the famous Olympic marksmen Malcolm Cooper helped to design, have been developed especially for use by those who want the best shot patterns over a wide range of distances.

The most successful model is the AW (Arctic Warfare) offered in calibers of 5.56x45 mm (.223 Remington) and 7.62x51 mm (.308 Winchester) and with a standard barrel length of 26 inches. The butt is produced from two pieces of Zytel (a plastic derivative) joined together and includes a front attachment for a bipod. In those versions with an adjustable shoulder strap and corner piece, the butt can be adapted to the ergonomics of the marksmen and a

viewfinder with a magnifying power of 6 or 10 can be attached on its upper end.

A later version of the AW bolt action rifle is the AWM which has been fitted with a replacement chamber for .300 Winchester Magnum catridges or 8.6x70 mm (.338 Lapua Magnun) cartridges. These weapons weigh about 15 pounds and have room for five cartridges. They can also be ordered with stepped or smooth barrels, a baffler or a silencer and even a butt that folds over to the left to reduce its length.

The latest model to arrive on the production line is the AW50 offered with a fixed butt called F or a collapsible one known as FT. It is designed to fire the powerful

Guillie suit
This is the general name for the special uniform worn by select marksmen. It is made from different materials that allow the marksman to conceal himself in a variety of environments.

Pairs

Military marksmen normally work in pairs where one person aims the weapon and the other is in charge of confirming the results of the shot in the viewfinder. The second soldier may also provide protection by using the assault rifle he carries.

12.70x99 mm (.50 Browning) cartridge against targets located at about 5,000 feet, for which it uses a Schmidt & Bender 3-12x50 MkII viewfinder with a Mil Dot reticule and protection against laser beams.

The basic weapon weighs 30 lbs and is 19 inches long, making it heavy and difficult to maneuver, especially taking into account that it must be carried by a member of the special forces. For this rea-son, a variant is being manufactured with a collapsible butt that measures 8 inches and weighs more than 2 lbs less, and another version is being developed with a titanium seal to reduce the final weight.

Compact and powerful

The Barrett M95 weapon is a bolt action rifle with powerful .50 Browning cartridges which enable it to hit targets located 6,000 feet away; it is also known for its compact size and weight.

The 700 Series
A majority of the U.S Special Forces and those in other countries trust derivations of the Remington 700 bolt action rifle for high precision shots at short or medium distances where its .308 caliber is the most effective.

Accuracy up to 1.25 miles

There are many other models on the market that use the same munitions as the model above. Some are also equipped with multipurpose projectiles designed to destroy minimally protected targets, projectiles for penetrating armor-plated vehicles or incendiary projectiles designed to cause severe damage to a target. During the Gulf War, two men with munitions of little more than a dollar each destroyed two armored vehicles valued at three million dollars, while the crew of another two in the column retreated terrified at not knowing from where or with what they were being attacked.

The U.S. firms of Barrett and McMillan also make excellent mo-

dels. Barrett has sold its M82A1 semiautomatic rifles throughout the world since their success in Operation Desert Storm in Kuwait and Iraq. Its design has facilitated the reduction of the recoil so that it is similar to that of a 12/70 hunting cartridge, and the ten cartridges in its clip can be fired off rapidly. Barrett also manufactures the M90 series which, along with the M95 and M99, are compact bolt action rifles measuring only 24 feet. Its

compact size was an important factor in the Spanish Army's decision to acquire it for their special forces.

McMillan has sold its M-87 and M-88 bolt action rifles to the U.S. Special Operations Command and to the French, who have used them in Bosnia against Serbian snipers. Their production line includes the single shot M-88ELR, which only weighs 23.8 lbs, the M-93 with a collapsible butt and the M-92 with a bull pup configuration.

Another manufacturer with an excellent reputation worldwide is the firm Robar from Phoenix that produces several models of bolt action rifles known for their excellent finish and low recoil. The French company Hecate has also continued improving its products to satisfy the requirements of its most demanding clients.

French model
The FR-F is a bolt action rifle which has been used by the French Special Forces for many years. It is lightweight and ergonomic due to modifications made to the original design

The Spanish Army has inherited a long tradition of guerrilla warfare. The tradition was begun when the first inhabitants of the Iberian peninsula fought against the various foreigners that tried to invade them over the years. This culture, strengthened by the country's mountainous geography and the character of its inhabitants, gave birth in the 1950's to a military specialty which was developed to integrate some army troops into the techniques of guerrilla warfare.

This concept has continued progressing over the years toward a technical professionalism regarding assigned missions, possibilities for use and the capacity of its participants. These changes have culminated in the creation of a Spanish special operations command center, the Mando de Operaciones Espe-

Mastery of the water
The Spanish green berets are qualified to move without restrictions in the water. To accomplish this, they are familiar with diving techniques and how to navigate all types of vessels.

ciales (MOE), currently stationed in Jaca, although it will be moved to the province of Alicante in the year 2000.

The C ommand Center

MOE is run by a colonel who is qualified in special operations and holds the general staff specialization. It was developed as a result of the changes applied to Plan NORTE, a program that has undertaken various adjustments in the organization, approach, level of force and available resources of the army to guarantee its operational capacity.

Facing the challenge of creation

The dissolution of some Grupos de Operaciones Especiales (GOE's) and the independent special operations companies stationed on the Balearic and Canary

Islands was undertaken at the same time as a process of evaluation of new capacities. This coincided with the start of deployments in Bosnia which saw the participation of a special operations team (NOE). It was division general José López Hijós, then deputy director of the Fuerza de Maniobra (FMA), who, after various studies and meetings that took place during the first months of 1997 between the commanders of the units that hadn't been dissolved, started the reform process that culminated in the creation of the MOE.

This command center, formed by government decree 184/1997 on October 6,1997, was integrated into the support team of the FMA and brought under the command of its commander in chief. The same publication described the center's missions: command of the Unidades de Operaciones Especiales (UOE's) in its charge and technical assessment of the training of all UOE's in the army. In addition, it must contribute to its

Use of explosives
The Spanish green berets are capable of calculating the place where they should store their explosive charges and the configuration required to destroy the target. They can also activate the explosive by a variety of different methods.

own planning and control and collaborate in the research, experimentation and development of the specific procedures and materials of the UOE's. It receives functional support from the training and doctrine command, Mando de Adiestramiento y Doctrina (MADOC), of the Spanish Army.

On November 30, 1999, government decree 272/1999 was published. The decree considered an opportune move of the MOE base to Rabasa in Alicante and contemplated the necessity concentrating all the subordinate units, thus initiating a change of position in the year 2000.

At this time, these changes have not affected the internal organization of the MOE, divided into a headquarters and three UOE's. The headquarters is the managing branch of the MOE and is led by a colonel and supported by a Staff Officers Command, an Experience Unit and a Staff Officers Company.

On any terrain
The training of the Spanish special troops is carried out on various types of terrain including mountains, rivers and snow-covered ground; this demands excellent physical fitness and a thorough understanding of the terrain.

The Staff Officers Command includes a communications headquarters, health services, a paymaster, and the departments of Information (Intelligence and Security), Operations (Training and Plans), Logistics and Personnel.

The Experience Unit consists of a commander in chief, eight officers and seventeen junior officers, all of whom have a wealth of experience in special operations units. Their professional experience is a vital part of the four specialized teams that make up the unit: infiltration by air, combat in the water, special materials and mountain combat. The specialists are the basis of the formation of highly capable tactical patrols that act as reinforcements for the UOE's and make up the operational core of those missions which require the deployment of subordinate units.

The Special Operation Company of the Staff Officers has a captain in charge and a staff of four officers, eighteen junior officers and 37 soldiers that work in the departments

Indirect fire
ECIA Commando 60 mm light mortar can reach scattered targets within a radius of .6 miles. Two well-trained men can fire a half a dozen grenades in fifteen seconds and retreat to a secure position.

Since 1957, this center has provided the training that has qualified about 1,500 soldiers, including those from other armies and countries, to lead and train future guerrilla fighters. In the year 2000, the 45th edition of the Advanced Aptitude Course for the Special Operations Units

Communications
The operational base and information and combat patrols are permanently linked thanks to the use of various communications systems including the new PR4G with a frequency jump module.

of Supply, Command, Maintenance and Communications. All of them work as a support team for the operations of headquarters and may also be used to back up the command of the FMA when it has to engage in special operations.

Command training
   Jaca is home to a school for training in maneuvering over mountains during special operations, the Escuela Militar de Montaña y Operaciones Especiales (EMMOE).

GVN-401 NIGHT VISION GOGGLES

The Spanish firm ENOSA, also known as INDRA EW since its latest restructuring, manufactures various models of night vision systems in its Madrid factory. This includes the GVN-401, which the Spanish Army purchased a thousand units of in 1995 for 900 million pesetas.

This model is made up of a skullcap and a sensory monocle with an improved tube. When it is not being used, it is kept in a waterproof plastic cover attached to the belt. It works by amplifying the surrounding light and has an active infrared focus which facilitates vision in closed areas or in total darkness.

The system is powered by two LR6 1.5 voltage alkaline batteries and weighs 29 ounces. It has a field of vision of 40°, works for 24 hours without needing to be recharged and is guaranteed to function in temperatures ranging from -13°F to +125.6°F. The oculars can be adjusted from +2 to –6 diopters so as to adapt to the operator's vision.

Command will begin. The course starts, after a strict selection process, at the beginning of September and ends in June of the following year upon completion of nine months of intense training.

Studies are divided into a basis initial phase, a second phase during which various subjects are taught and a third part of practical applications. The initial phase is made up of a review of general military knowledge and various tests with obstacles on the application field and in a maze of underground tunnels called the "conguito". In addition, they also practice martial arts and self-defense, do topographic exercises using a compass and the Global Position System and learn to operate communications equipment.

The second phase deals with climbing, parachuting (at the Escuela Militar de Paracaidismo Méndez Parada in Alcantarilla in the province of Murcia), combat in snowy areas where skis or snowshoes are necessary, firing various types of weapons and calculations associated with the use of explosives. It also teaches hand to hand combat, infiltration using survival techniques and infiltration by water, which usually takes place in the town of L'Escala and ranges from maneuvering vessels to deep sea diving with oxygen tanks.

The course ends with a complex exercise lasting several days during which most of the previous subject matter is put into practice. To make it more difficult, special operations companies are deployed on the battlefield to try to capture the trainees.

Operational capacity

Several factors contribute to the survival of these small units of special forces: the predisposition of the men that make up the special operations units, their experience in combat during the first half of the 1970's and in the Sahara and the qualities of toughness, sacrifice and resistance inherent to all Spaniards.

These units are known for their excellent cost efficiency because they are especially trained in the

techniques of insertion and extraction, and they don't use large deployments of vehicles, but rather a small unit of four-wheel-drive vehicles and 3 or 4 ton trucks. In addition, they are trained to fire weapons and engage in combat, travel over all types of terrain and swim up rivers and reservoirs – all cost efficient activities compared with the necessities of a large mechanized unit.

Operational units

General regulation 2/98 for Organic Adaptations established that, by July 1, 1998, the GOE Valencia III in Alicante, the 3rd Ampurdán IV in Barcelona and the Maderal Oleaga XIX BOEL in

Helicopter support
The army's aircraft forces often support the actions of the green berets with various models of helicopters in which they transport them to the points where they will initiate ground infiltrations.

Light machine gun
The AMELI is a highly accurate light 5.56x45 mm machine gun which is currently being integrated into Spanish commando units.

Málaga would be integrated into the MOE.

Each of the former groups is commanded by a colonel and supported by an organization composed of a Staff Officers Command, a Staff Officers Company and two COE's for a total of 250 men, of which 100 are command and the rest are professional troops. One of the COE's specializes in special reconnaissance missions and the other in direct actions. During missions, the operational teams split up into small groups of four or six men for observation and patrols of up to twenty men to attack.

The Direct Action COE is composed of a command, a unit of high precision marksmen (FTT), a squad in charge of 60 mm light mortar, and three Equipos Operativos

(EO's) for pure combat missions against all types of targets. Each EO is subdivided into three basic teams (EB) made up of equal numbers of command and personnel.

The Reconnaissance COE is organized into a command patrol and twelve special reconnaissance patrols (PRE) in charge of surveillance of targets and reporting any pertinent information to the patrol base. The COE of the Staff Officers Comapny is structured in much the same way as that of the MOE, but it has a greater number of men.

The regulation for the use of the army (DO1-001) mandates that both the PRE and EB be composed of six men. The commanding officer must be joined by another in charge of the unit who also acts as navigator. In addition, both units should have a variety of specialists in charge of preparation of explosives, handling communications equipment, high precision shooting and treating accidents or wounds.

These units are responsible for a variety of actions including hand to

Air insertion
All of the commanding officers and a majority of the troops are qualified in automatic parachuting, an activity which enables them to arrive at the point of combat rapidly and accurately.

hand combat, indicating targets to be attacked by all types of weapons, maneuvering special munitions by computer and military assistance. They might also have to capture and eliminate important enemy personnel, capture targets, rescue their own personnel from enemy hands, evaluate the damage caused after an attack, keep watch over vulnerable areas or cut off enemy communications lines. In addition, they can carry out complementary missions such as military assessments, protection of authority figures, psychological warfare, Non-combatant Evacuation Operations (NEO) and humanitarian aid activities such as those undertaken in the former Yugoslavia.

More powerful equipment

The Spanish special units use equipment very similar to that of the rest of the army, but they are also equipped with some special materials. A program has been put in place to acquire more powerful weapons, and it should be completed in the first few years of the 21st century. It includes new weapons such as automatic rifles and shotguns and improved personnel equipment capable of withstanding severe weather conditions and harsh surroundings.

Specialized legionaries
The Bandera de Operaciones Especiales de La Legión (BOEL) is a group of green berets qualified to operate on any terrain. They are equipped with desert uniforms to camouflage themselves in arid zones.

SPAIN: SPECIAL OPERATIONS COMMAND

Centralized Command
The MOE and the Staff Officers Companies of the groups and the BOEL are charged with the basic activity of organizing and leading the missions of the subordinate information and combat units by using complex coordination centers.

Military uniforms include the standard camouflage complete with tactical vest, the green beret that is normally substituted for a wide-brimmed hat in the army, Camel-back water canteens and Bianchi UM-84 covers. Personnel elements also include a white camouflage suit for the snow and Kevlar protective equipment (Mars helmet and anti-shrapnel vest). There are also individual protective elements for use in environments contaminated with nuclear, biological or chemical agents, and Nemrod wetsuits and compressed air and oxygen tanks for deep sea diving. In addition, they are provided with skiing and climbing equipment, kayaks and Zodiac or IBS pneumatic vessels used for aquatic activities.

Communications links are assured by systems such as the

Special reconaissance
A patrol, generally of four or sic men can enter anemy territory to observe vital points and transport zones and send data via their ownband with the support of sophisticated communication systems.

GVN-401 NIGHT GOGGLES

The National Optics Company (ENOSA), also known as INDRA EW since latest restructuring produces differents night vision systems at its factory in Aranjuez (Madrid), including the GWN (Night Vision Goggles) 401. The Spanish ground Army acqyired a million units in 1995 for 4 1/2 million follars. Thisa model is made up of a headpiece and a monocular sight with a built-in and improved 11th generation tube.

When not being used, they are kept in a plastic and watertight case that is fixed to the belst. They operate passively with ambiental light amplifications and include an associated active infrared spotlight for seeing in enclosed or pitch-black places.

The system is powered by two 1.5 volt LR6 alkaline batteries and the total weight es 823 g. Their field of visions is of 40º, they are autonomous for 24 hours fo use and they are guaranteed to work in a range of temperatures from -25º up to 52º C. The oculars are adjustable from +2 to -6 gradations for adaptation to the user's vison.

Thompson PR4G with a frequency jump module, the BCC-349 for links with patrols, the AN/PRC-74-B and UK/PRC-320 radio stations and the MEROD PSV-1642-M digital terminal for coded transmissions.

Individual and group armaments are in the process of being replaced by weapons such as the Heckler und Köck G-36E/K 5.56x45 mm assault rifle, automatic rifles and pistols from the same

firm and pump action shotguns. Meanwhile, they continue to use Llama M82 pistols and Star Z-70 9x19 mm automatic rifles, CETME 5.56 assault rifles in three different versions, AMELI .223 Remington light machine guns and Accuracy AW 7.62x51 mm and Barrett M95 12.70x99 high precision rifles. They are also equipped with MG42 .308 Winchester medium machine guns, Instalaza M65 rocket launchers and C-90C/CR disposable grenade launchers and

ECIA 60 mm mortars. Some of these models have attachments for ENOSA VNP-009, ANVS700, Simrad KN202 and Pilkington Optronics night vision viewfinders. Equipment for special missions includes ENOSA GVN-201 and 401 night vision goggles, TacStar TULP laser lights, Aimpoint red point viewfinders, silencers for AW rifles, Barnett Commando crossbows, hand grenades, Coruña flare pistols and all types of explosives.

The training process that a member of a special operations unit must go through lasts several years and is divided into an initial period of technical training and another phase of exercises during which he puts into practice all that he has learned. In order to maneuver easily and complete missions successfully, it is fundamental to understand the techniques of concealment which enable one to take advantage of natural and personal resources to hide from enemy surveillance (patrols, seismic sensors, thermal cameras and antipersonnel radar). In addition, soldiers must learn how to obtain the food and water needed to survive during reconnaissance missions behind enemy lines or when escaping from unfamiliar territory after an attack on a significant enemy target.

Knowing how to hide

Special military actions can be dynamic, when attacking a target, or static, when doing surveillance work from a specific position. In both cases, extra care must be taken to guarantee the concealment of the operational equipment from enemy

Difficult mountainous areas
Members of commando units must be trained to survive in a variety of environments and confront the many difficulties encountered during their tactical deployments.

Black
Those missions that take place in aquatic or urban environments normally call for the use of black camouflage in the form of paint, ski masks, wetsuits and jumpsuits. This equipment is also used for night actions.

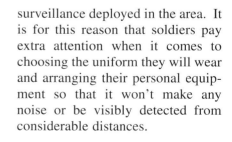

surveillance deployed in the area. It is for this reason that soldiers pay extra attention when it comes to choosing the uniform they will wear and arranging their personal equipment so that it won't make any noise or be visibly detected from considerable distances.

Taking many precautions
Many elements are available to a green beret to help him conceal himself during a mission: the tone, color and markings of his uniform, camouflage used on his arms and face to break up the regularity of the

profile, suits designed to dissipate body heat and avoid thermal contrasts, elements responsible for decreasing the electromagnetic waves given off by the equipment and silencers that diminish the banging associated with the firing of weapons.

All of this implies an exhaustive preparation of the assigned mission, personal equipment and methods of concealment such as camouflage nets and blocks of mud to partially cover one's position. This process generally calls for the use of low cost methods, camouflage paint and old uniforms ripped in shreds to make Guillie suits, used in conjunction with more advanced equipment such as transmitters of specific frequencies which alter the enemy's sensor readings or neutralize the search capacity of dogs trained to locate people (pepper scattered by a patrol can also be very useful in putting bloodhounds off the scent).

Methods of concealment

To conceal one's own presence,

natural or artificial methods may be used in relation to the type of terrain —snow-covered, desert, forest or

The best camouflage

Combat uniforms and equipment used by soldiers are designed to provide them with the best camouflage when deployed on the ground. The camouflage tones used vary from army to army.

Using nature

Soldiers qualified in special operations should known which resources they can obtain and use as sustenance in every type of environment where there is no other food available.

urban. Natural methods, such as mud or vegetation, are useful because they don't cost anything, are easy to find in some areas and are very effective. Artificial means require an intense industrial effort to develop, but are offered in a wide range of elements specifically designed for camouflage.

The soldier should have at his disposal several uniforms with camouflage adapted to the terrain of the combat area. Forests require markings similar in tone and shape to the surrounding environment, and a white uniform with some black stripes to break up the monotone is used on snow-covered terrain. A light brown uniform is suitable for the desert and for urban environments, black is best when working

at night. Camouflage paint and ointments are also applied to the face and uncovered areas in relation to the terrain and chosen uniform, but the use of products that omit odors different to those of the body are carefully avoided.

Belts, backpacks and other personal equipment should be chosen along the same lines as the uniform, taking special care with how they are arranged so as to avoid making any noise. It is also important to wear water-resistant fabrics or those that protect against the cold. Other materials available to these special units are camouflage nets made of materials that absorb radar waves,

Difficult to find
The members of special units who act as snipers normally use nets and special uniforms to camouflage themselves from enemy patrols.

metallic blankets that conceal body heat, picks and spades for digging concealment trenches and sensors designed as passive elements.

Capacity for self-sufficiency
The types of missions assigned to commando groups imply that they will sometimes have to face emergency situations resulting from the failure of extraction operations. During these periods, they will probably have to go for long periods of time without any new supplies and avoid intensive search campaigns by enemy forces.

Professional adaptation
In these and other situations, soldiers must have the skills to confront the enemy using all the means available to them. This not only means the use of technical methods, but also the psychological resistance to overcome situations of demoralization, frustration, stress and fatigue.

Deployment in Norway
Soldiers from some countries, like this one from Holland, do some of their training in Norway in order to understand the possibilities for action in severe weather conditions and extremely cold temperatures.

The professional qualifications of these individuals enable them to overcome the negative circumstances of the terrain and take from the land anything that might be useful to them. This involves a fundamental know-ledge of the terrain, which the green berets receive in training. The survival phase of training includes deployment in a variety of areas such as the sea, the desert and the forest so that the soldiers learn the peculiarities of each and how to counteract the humidity, cold or heat they will suffer while maneuvering within them.

Training should include deployments on all types of terrain, navigation skills, and information on ways to construct a shelter, make fire and obtain water to maintain a minimum level of body hydration. In addition, soldiers should learn emergency first-aid techniques, how to be self-sufficient in feeding themselves and how to read the signs of approaching meteorological conditions.

Personal experience is very useful when it comes to operational maneuvers, preparing equipment to be deployed in a given area and evaluating factors, like luck, which could influence the final result of the mission. A detailed plan is also very important prior to undertaking any mission as it calculates the time needed to complete tasks, prepares alternative plans and evaluates all necessities.

Psychological resistance

Training should also take into account the psychological techniques associated with survival as human behavior varies in relation to specific external stimuli.

Techniques that can contribute greatly to the overall success of a mission include overcoming the fear associated with an especially difficult situation, knowing how to control one's impulses to avoid capture

Survival skills
The members of the Tercio special operations group from Ampurdán normally take part in several phases of survival training every year. This allows them to put into practice the techniques learned to use natural resources to feed themselves over a limited period of time.

when enemy forces are nearby, resisting enemy interrogation so as to give away a minimum amount of information and maintaining a high

morale regarding the victory of the mission.

The will to survive is also very important as it enables the individual to confront and overcome the various conditions found during deployment. In a risky situation, a soldier must keep calm and free of tension so as to use the skills he has learned to resolve the problem.

Therefore, the training processes for the special units in many armies and countries are long and specific enough so as to discern which individuals exhibit the best psychological qualifications and which are not suitable even though they possess impeccable technical skills. It is vitally important to select the most qualified soldiers in terms of the practical necessities of the contingent.

Simple techniques
One of the skills that every member of a commando unit should know is the preparation of various types of shelters using the surrounding nature —anything from tents constructed from branches to igloos made from blocks of ice.

SEAL'S: THE COMMANDOS OF THE AMERICAN NAVY

The American Navy, headed by the Chief of Naval Operations (CNO), is made up of various surface vessel and submarine forces supported by air units and combat groups. This last section includes the famous Navy SEAL's (Sea, Air and Land), soldiers whose training and preparation enables them to carry out special military missions anywhere in the world. Among the missions they have participated in is a collaborative effort with the Department of Energy to train security teams to protect U.S. nuclear installations and prepare contingency plans to confront any terrorist threats to these highly valuable strategic centers.

Tactical simulation
This shows a team of men from SEAL Team 8 ready to participate in a simulation that requires the launching of divers from a helicopter to assault a factory which manufactures chemical products.

Proven capacity

These commando groups, composed of Navy troops, have an excellent worldwide reputation, and they are frequently deployed in the most controversial areas of the planet to carry out a variety of missions in support of the global interests of the United States. They also collaborate on a regular basis with similar units of ally countries in joint exercises and maneuvers as a way of sharing experiences, techniques and special procedures.

A long history

Their origins date back to the Scout and Raider units that participated in the invasion of North Africa in 1942, from the volunteers of the Naval Construction Battalion that helped to clear obstacles from

the path of the amphibious groups invading Sicily in 1943 and from the assault on Normandy in 1944. Another decisive factor was the decision, by Admiral Ernest J. King, who was Chief of Naval Operations in 1943, to create the Naval Combat Demolition Unit (NCDU) led by Draper L. Kauffmen.

Men who were selected to participate in these missions had excellent physical fitness, courage and survival skills. Their missions included hydrographic reconnaissance before assaults, activities which were entrusted to Underwater Demolition Teams (UDT) trained in Fort Pierce, Florida and Maui. These professionals, known as frogmen, also distinguished themselves during the Korean War where they carried out reconnaissance on bridges only accessible from the water and searched for mines.

As the capacities of the UDT's increased, their missions included direct actions, demolitions, guerril-

Coastal patrol boats
Cyclone PC's can deploy more than 300 metric tons and have been designed to transport SEAL units. The men access the water by the bow, which is especially fitted for this reason.

la warfare, combat operations and the capture of information from enemy territory. A special training process prepared the men to carry out these missions. On January 1, 1962, President John F. Kennedy signed certain documents authorizing the increase of military capacities to carry out unconventional warfare missions. As a result, SEAL teams 1 and 2 were created from UDT troops.

Their principal mission was to carry out anti-guerrilla warfare and clandestine operations in the sea and on the banks of rivers and marshes, and they were immediately deployed in the jungles of Southeast Asia during the Vietnam War. The Seal's and UDT's worked hand in hand with the

Special Boat Units (SBS) until the conflict ended in 1975. They also participated in multiple actions that led to the elimination of close to a thousand Vietcong (580 of them have been officially recognized) and resulted in 48 casualties of their own.

The UDT's, both the combat teams and those responsible for deploying the transport vehicles associated with their activities, were dissolved in May 1983 and converted into SEAL's. Their most recent actions (some of them top secret) include participation in Operation Urgent Fury in 1983 during which the island of Granada was liberated, the rescue of passengers from the Italian ship Achille Lauro, hijacked in 1985 by

Attacks in the desert
The Chenworth DPV (Desert Patrol Light Strike Vehicle) is a light four-wheel-drive vehicle which can move across any type of terrain with a weapons systems attached to a stand at the rear.

RIB VESSEL

Since 1997, the Navy has purchased 70 NSW RIB (Navy Special Warfare Rigid Inflatable Boat) manufactured by United States Marine Incorporated (USMI) in their production plant in New Orleans.

These boats, transported on a special flat bed, are pneumatic vessels with a fiberglass hull optimized to reach speeds of up to 52 mph or 45 knots. They have two inboard Caterpillar motors with 470 horsepower, which are attached to two Kamewa FF280 hydrojets that serve as engines. They are controlled by one of their three crew members, all of whom tra-

vel in seats next to the central console, which includes a Furuno navigational radar system placed on an upper stand. The stern has room for eight men to travel in comfortable individual seats.

The vessel is 36 feet long, 10.5 feet wide and has a draft of 3 feet. It has a range of 200 miles, and its total weight, loaded with a cargo of 660 lbs, exceeds 8 metric tons. The stern and bow each have a weapons stand so that various weapons systems can be used to cover the vessel's maneuvers.

Palestinian terrorists, and Operation Earnest Will, which took place between 1987 and 1990 in the Persian Gulf and was aimed at neutralizing Iranian activities and oil rigs. In addition, the SEAL's took part in Operation Just Cause, which culminated in the invasion of Panama in 1989 to overthrow and capture General Noriega and, in 1990 and 1991, in Operations Shield and Desert Storm for the liberation of Kuwait from Iraqi occupation. They have also participated in recent missions in Somalia, Haiti, Liberia and Bosnia. In Bosnia, they carried out actions such as reconnaissance and the seizing of the hydrographic charts necessary to build a bridge over the Sava River, allowing U.S. forces to move from Croatia to Bosnia Herzegovina.

Special naval command

On April 16, 1987 the NAVSPECWARCOM (Naval

Special Warfare Command or NSWC) was created and established on the Coronado navy base in San Diego. It is presently under the joint command of the United States Special Operations Command (USSOCOM) located on the McDill air force base in Tampa.

Naval Special Warfare Group (NSWG) 1, responsible for the Pacific and Persian Gulf zones, and 2, responsible for the Atlantic, European and South American zones, fall under the command of the NSWC, which directs the activities of six thousand men in the active and reserve troops. NSWG-1 is based in Coronado and is composed of Naval Special Warfare Unit (NSWU) 1 and 3, SEAL Delivery Vehicles (SDV) Unit 1 and SEAL teams 1, 3 and 5. NSWG-2 works out of Little Creek, Virginia and is made up of SDV 2, SEAL's 2, 4 and 8, and NSWU 2 from Great Britain, 4 from Puerto Rico and 10 from Spain.

Working as a support force for the NSWG-1 is Special Boat Regiment (SBR) 1, which includes

Firepower
M60E3 medium machine guns are some of the weapons used by SEAL's during their missions. They are capable of firing 800 7.62x51 mm munitions per minute.

Special Boat Unit (SBU) 12 and four Patrol Craft (PC) groups. NSWG-2 collaborates with SBR 2, which is composed of 9 PC's and SBU's 20, 22 and 26. The Naval Special Warfare Development Group (NSWDG) from Dam Neck, Virginia supports all of the previous special forces by providing a center for special training and the testing of new equipment.

Every SEAL team is made up of 10 squads of sixteen men each, a headquarters which coordinates their activities, and a support cell of about twenty men. Each squad includes two commanding officers and fourteen soldiers split up into two squads of eight; each of these squads is then divided into two combat units, and then divided once more into two teams of two men each.

Each group works in a specific area. SEAL 1 is assigned to Southeast Asia, 2 works in northern Europe, 3 in the Mid-East, 4 in South America, 5 in South Korea and 8 in Africa. In addition, SEAL 6 is located at the Fleet Combat Training Center in Dam Neck and participates in counter terrorist and rescue missions for the Navy.

At the beginning of 1999, various proceedings were organized to work toward a restructuring of these elite forces so as to adapt them to the needs of the 21st century; these changes will be introduced progressively.

Ample materials at their disposal
The generous economic means of the U.S Navy make it possible to

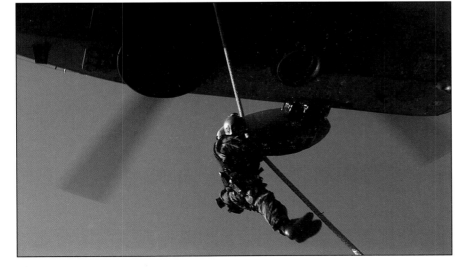

Fast rope
The simple technique of sliding down a thick rope attached to a helicopter in stationary flight allows SEAL commandos to reach the ground quickly and safely.

purchase all the necessary elements they need for the successful completion of their commando missions during the day or at night all over the world; this implies a substantial financial contribution from the USSOCOM. The arsenals of the SEAL's, which include fixed deployments in various positions all over the globe and in naval fleets in the world's oceans, contain all the materials necessary for their assigned missions –special reconnaissance, direct actions, unconventional warfare, antiterrorist activities and international defense.

Total mobility
U.S. Navy boats and airplanes transport SEAL teams to the position from which they will begin their mission; for this reason, soldiers are continuously training with various models of helicopters.

A variety of armaments

The nature of the missions assigned to the SEAL's demands a wide range of light weapons that can be deployed in relation to the requirements of any given moment. Soldiers are normally equipped with Sig Sauer P226 9x19 mm Parabellum pistols, Heckler und Köch (H&K) MP5N automatic rifles with fixed or retractable butt and M4 5.56x45 mm (.223 Remington) carbines, manufactured by various firms including Colt Firearms.

M203 40 mm single-shot grenade launchers are usually attached to the weapons previously described. Short and long weapons also have attachments for Sure-Fire spotlights, visible or infrared lasers and red point aiming mechanisms such as the Swedish Simpoint Comp-M or the American Trijicom Acog. In addition, they use H&K

Manual parachutes
Training for many members of the U.S Navy SEAL's includes parachute jumps with manual openings, which are more discreet and better at reaching targets accurately.

MK23 model 0 .45 ACP pistols with silencer and illumination module, .22 Long Rifle small semi-automatic weapons with integrated silencer and M16A2 assault rifles which fire the same munitions as the M4. Their wide range of short arms includes the Smith & Wesson model 686 "Distinguished" revolver with a 357 Magnum caliber and H&K P-9S and Beretta M-92F 9x19 mm pistols.

Among the more powerful weapons are the M-249 SAW (Squad Automatic Weapon) light machine guns with room for 200 .223 Remington cartridges, lightweight Saco M-60E3 7.62x51 mm (.308 Winchester) medium machine guns and M-2HB (High Barrel) 12.70x99 mm (.50 Browning) heavy machine guns. These last two models are normally situated on stands in light, highly mobile vehicles or on sea vessels. For highly accurate shots, there are numerous models of rifles in their arsenals: Remington 700 bolt action and semiautomatic M-

SIG SAUER P226 PISTOL

The pistol was designed at the beginning of the 1980's for a contest in new semiautomatic weapons sponsored by the U.S. Armed Forces. Although it was not selected at that time, many special units, military groups and police forces have used this design by the Swiss firm SIG. It has an excellent finish, an accurate ergonomic configuration and has been tested for mechanical reliability under harsh conditions.

The weapon, largely based on the P220 configuration, has an empty weight of 26.5 ounces, a length of 7.7 inches and room for 15 or 20 9x19 mm

Parabellum cartridges securely carried in the chamber. One pump action version is manufactured from blued steel, more resistant to corrosion, which is used by the SEAL's.

They are normally transported in a leg cover next to a Laser Products attachment, which can be placed on the front end of the handguard to hold a powerful Sure-Fire spotlight. This spotlight produces an intensely powerful light switched on by an activator on the handle. The system, which weighs 10.5 ounces, is submergible up to depths of 165 feet.

14, M-21 and SR-25 rifles (all with .308 caliber), McMillan M-86SR .300 Winchester Magnum rifles and McMillan M-88 and Barret M82A1 rifles with .50 Browning caliber.

Other firearms at their disposal are Mossberg pump action rifles, MK-19 model 3 40 mm automatic grenade launchers, 60 and 81 mm mortars, AT-4 and M72 LAW disposable rocket launchers and the M3 Carl Gustav 84 mm anti-tank missile system.

The best equipment

Naval commandos stock up with a large quantity of wardrobe items as part of their personal equipment. These range from desert boots for arid climates to three-quarter length Gore-Tex jackets for protection from the cold and wet. Combined with the Battle Dress Uniform (BDU) and depending on individual tastes, there are shirts, bulletproof vests, ProTec helmets, gloves for sliding down ropes quickly, all kinds of boots, wetsuits, camouflage uniforms, belts that can attach a variety of leg covers

depending on the type of weapon and method of transport, small money belts for personal items and a variety of other things.

More advanced pieces of equipment include communications systems with high frequency bands for long distance links and portable antennas for satellite links, deep sea diving equipment such as tanks of compressed air and Dräguer LAR V oxygen tanks and automatic and manual parachuting materials. In addition, they use global position systems (GPS) and a wide range of observational and night vision elements such as AN/PVS-7C monocle goggles, which can be worn underwater.

Airborne containers carry all the equipment and armaments neces-

Naval boarding

SEAL's must carry out missions of detaining ships suspected of transporting highly dangerous materials or of carrying weapons in conflict zones. This involves boarding the ship to control the crew and requisition the cargo.

Insertion

CPC MkV vessels are small aluminum boats designed to transport reduced numbers of SEAL groups, who normally travel in the interior of the structure with their equipment underneath in the hull. A ramp extended from the stern facilitates the movements of these pneumatic vessels.

sary for exercises and maneuvers. Transportation means also include modern light trucks with small standardized cabins, which can tow various types of pneumatic vessels, or Chenworth DPV (Desert Patrol Light Strike Vehicles), vehicles used in deep reconnaissance missions which have numerous attachments for any type of weapons system assigned to the three crew members.

Underwater support is given by Mk VIII or ASDS SDV (SEAL Delivery Vehicle) mini submarines, machines that are normally transported to the deployment zone in cylindrical containers attached to the submarine deck. These small submarines

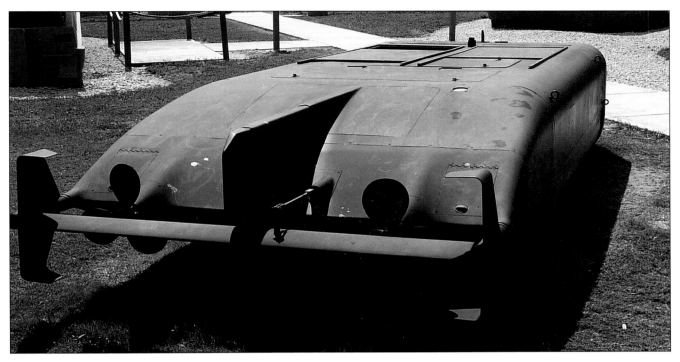

Mini submarines
SDV's (SEAL Delivery Vehicle), like this Mark IX, have been designed to carry small groups of men comfortably and rapidly from their means of transport (generally a nuclear submarine) to a coastal point in enemy territory.

Stalker with speeds of up to 53 knots and the Stinger RPB (River Patrol Boat). Those missions that require air deployments use Air Force transport planes or Navy helicopters such as the AB-212, CH-46 Sea Knight, SH-3D Sea King and CH-53 Sea Stallion.

Protection
Pro-Tech helmets are widely distributed among SEAL units because their configuration and plastic make-up protects the head from the effects of any collisions suffered during rapid movements. A strobe light can be attached to the top to facilitate their localization if they fall into the water.

require several hours and the efforts of numerous personnel before they are prepared for transport missions that can last up to 6 or 8 hours. For surface use, there are RIB (Rigid Inflatable Boats) or CRRC (Combat Rubber Raiding Craft) or Cyclone PC (Patrol Craft) patrol boats, which can transport 328 tons and are heavily armed to support the deployment of up to 9 commando groups. They also use the new CPC (Coastal Patrol Craft) MkV, which is made of aluminum and can be transported in the cargo hold of plane, the C-17, the Sea

Almost every country maintains small groups specialized in various aspects of parachute jumping. Some form large paratrooper units and others work independently as special commando forces or subordinate units.

The professional preparation of these soldiers, the missions they carry out, their value as special forces and other important factors make them a very useful part of special actions.

Special training

Training begins with an initial phase of physical strengthening and is followed by instruction in skills such as concealment, survival, first aid, communications, navigation and patrol maneuvers.

The parachute jump

In the first week of training soldiers learn basic jumping skills, review the various models of para-chutes, prepare to tackle problems and move about the fuselage of the plane (or in simulated models) to familiarize themselves with the small space. They also practice their jumps from a tower so as to understand the effects of the fall and landing and learn to deal with situations in which the wind is dragging their parachute.

The next phase is dedicated to the technique and practice of parachute jumps. They must do between six and ten jumps to become certified in automatic parachuting. Soldiers are chosen to do the manual parachute

Prepared to jump
The Deep Reconnaissance Patrols (PRP's) of the Spanish Army's (BRI-PAC) are intended to be the eyes and the ears of the unit, and they are usually deployed before the other troops.

High altitudes
Those paratroopers qualified in the techniques of manual jumps are professionals capable of jumping from great heights provided they carry oxygen respiration equipment.

course, a more selective training with regard to the methods and inherent difficulty of the jump, based on their experiences in exercises and maneuvers and their personal qualities.

An exhaustive medical examination selects some candidates and excludes others who are not suitable. Those chosen will work for almost two months to learn all the relative information, and they will do about fifty jumps with manual parachutes used for training and operations such as the MT-1X.

Once they are assigned a base, they will continue practicing with other models of parachutes better suited to flying. Their training will include jumps during the day and at night, and they will almost always work in small groups.

Parachute jumping with oxygen

Those who wish to train in HAHO (High Altitude High Opening) or HALO (High Altitude Low Opening) jumps must submit to another medical examination and enter the barometric pressure chamber, which simulate flights at different altitudes. These jumps are made from between 23,000 and 33,000 feet. In HAHO jumps, the parachute opens immediately after jumping, while during HALO jumps, it doesn't open until the paratrooper falls to about 3,300 feet or when it is activated by a timed barometer.

The difficulty with these jumps is that the soldier must breathe oxygen out of tanks he has brought with him because the air is not breathable above 2.5 miles. This means he must adapt his breathing before

the jump by using a breathing machine fixed to the floor of the plane. The process of acclimatization, which eliminates nitrogen from the blood, lasts for more than an hour and requires breathing in 100% oxygen. Otherwise, variations in barometric pressure can expand the gases dissolved by the body and cause pain in the joints or even an embolism.

The paratrooper must also face extreme cold, going from a comfortable +50° in the interior of the plane to -58° outside at 30,000 feet. Furthermore, the cold increases with the wind and navigational speed of the parachute, requiring the use of special suits, usually Gore-Tex, that cover the entire body to protect it from the harsh conditions. Soldiers must also carry a heavy backpack, equipment and

NAVIGATIONAL CONSOLE

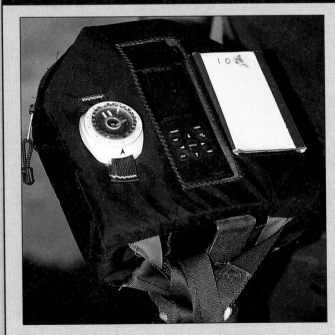

The paratrooper groups that infiltrate enemy territory via a manual parachute jump need an element to help them reach their selected landing point with maximum accuracy. Among the systems currently available on the market is this navigational console, which is used by patrol group leaders to ascertain the direction they are moving in.

The mechanism, which is attached to the paratrooper's chest so he can comfortably read it during the jump, includes a 4000XL GPS (Global Position System), manufactured by the U.S firm Maguellan, which receives information from various satellites. By triangulating the satellites, a soldier can determine his exact location and follow the planned route. The console also integrates a compass to ascertain the direction he is falling in and an attachment for documents concerning the parameters he should follow during the fall and the subsequent penetration.

armaments during a tactical jump.

Operational deployment

Among the most qualified European units in the types of Special Air Operations (SAO's) put forth in ATP documents by NATO are the Portuguese, Spanish, British and Swiss.

The Iberian Peninsula

The Portuguese Army maintains a group of paratroopers, known as SOGAS, specialized in HALO and HAHO manual jumps within its center for airborne troops. Their origins date back to a special forces company partially active in the Light Paratrooper Brigade of the Air Force. Subsequently, they were integrated into a Battalion for Air and Land Support and stationed at a training center responsible for everything related to parachute work: folding chutes, studying new materials, repairing equipment, preparing and launching cargo and marking landing zones.

The High Altitude Operational

Jumpers are part of a Company of Air and Ground Markers and are capable of infiltrating enemy lines to search for and establish landing points for their fellow paratroopers. This activity requires special tactical skills in reaching pre-established meeting points without being detected, employing special armaments to avoid capture, knowing how to use the environment to survive during deployments lasting for several days and working complex communications systems. Their personal equipment includes oxygen tanks, camouflage covers for transporting parachutes and Israeli Mini-Uzi automatic rifles.

The Spanish Air Force maintains a paratrooper unit, the Escuadrilla de Zapadores Paracaidistas (EZA-PAC), whose motto is "only those

Varied equipment
The French firm Zodiac manufactures equipment designed for use by the paratroopers in the French Armed Forces and by any other countries that wish to purchase it.

Jump into space
The tailgate in transport planes is generally the best place to carry out manual parachute jumps. The men only have to jump into space and open their chutes when they reach the proper height.

willing to die for a noble ideal deserve to live". Its headquarters in on the Alcantarilla Air Force Base in the province of Murcia, and it is composed of a commander-in-chief and almost two hundred professional soldiers divided among the departments of Operations, Logistical Support, Training, Services, Secretariat, Administration and Operational Teams.

Each operational team, known as SAO (Special Air Operations), includes fifteen men trained to carry out missions such as CCT (Combat Control Team) for directing air operations, rescuing injured soldiers or damaged equipment (CSAR), establishing networks of ground observations and FAC (Forward Air Controller) missions for designating and illuminating targets. They are also responsible for training air troops in the SERER techniques of evasion, escape, survival and protection of especially vulnerable points.

These missions require qualifications in HALO and HAHO parachute jumps and specialized equipment such as Litton laser signalers for marking targets, diving materials for deployments in the water and sophisticated communications equipment like the PR4G. They must also have a large supply of parachute models such as the Tandem for two people and a radio controlled one for carrying cargo up to 660 pounds.

The Brigada Paracaidista (BRIPAC) of the Spanish Army

Paratroopers
All armies maintain active small groups of specialized professionals trained in a variety of jump methods depending on the type of ground, combat or reconnaissance mission they are assigned.

Specialized groups
The U.S Navy SEAL's are composed of soldiers qualified in the techniques of manual parachute jumping for an accurate journey to the established landing zone.

has a special missions headquarters (JAE), which houses several Advanced Air Disembarkation Platoons (SADA's) and Deep Reconnaissance Patrols (PRP's) made up of highly qualified paratroopers. Trained in maneuvering across snow and in water, the men of the PRP can infiltrate enemy territory, usually from great heights, travelling up to 200 miles inside to obtain information. For their missions, they use TMP-Plus and G-9 parachutes, Phaos jump helmets with MBV 12P respiratory masks and oxygen tanks with a breathing time of 29 minutes or

30 miles of parachute gliding.

British specialists

Paratroopers from the United Kingdom specialized in air penetrations from high altitudes and large distances are called Pathfinders. They operate during the day or at night with CQ 360 parachutes, normally supporting other paratroopers by designating and illuminating landing spots and securing the perimeter from enemy assault. They are also capable of a variety of other special actions thanks to their ability to discreetly reach any point by jumping out of C-130 H and J Royal Air Force transport planes.

Journey to the target
These paratroopers occupy their seats in the fuselage of the transport plane that will take them to their jumping positions. Their equipment includes heavy packs for use during their deep reconnaissance mission.

Skilled in the techniques of sabotage and diving, they normally work in small patrols of 4 or 5 specialists with equipment and armaments especially adapted to their task. Their armaments include M-16 assault rifles with M203 grenade launchers attached to the handguard, GMPG 7.62 mm medium machine guns and AW high precision rifles. Some of the specialized equipment at their disposal are GPS Maguellan receivers, Berguen combat backpacks, altimeters which can be fixed to the left arm, suits for withstanding the low temperatures associated with parachuting, PRC-319 radio systems and night viewfinders. They also have the use of light Land Rovers especially modified for more comfortable and effective maneuvers.

The 31st Aviation Brigade of the Swiss Air Force has a unit called the Fernspähkompanie 17 composed of one hundred specialists in exploratory jumps with MT-1XX manual or T-10 automatic parachutes. Their mission is to form small teams of four or five men

Air insertion
Any launch pad, such as this P-3 Orión anti-submarine war plane, can be used by paratroopers to jump toward the point where they will begin their insertion into the target zone.

Oxygen console
HALO and HAHO parachute jumps require that the paratrooper first breathe into a console of mixed gases in order to adapt to the great height from which he will jump and be able to breathe in the oxygen he will carry in individual tanks.

spread across the country so that, in case of an invasion, they can report all enemy movements to headquarters. This task involves traveling at night and hiding during the day.

Initial training for these specialists lasts twenty-two weeks and is completed with a mountain phase and instruction on all types of weapons. These paratroopers carry

packs weighing more than 90 lbs with which they must march over 40 miles per day. They are armed with

STGW90 rifles from the firm SIG and have viewfinders, communications systems and concealment equipment. Switzerland's unique defense policy means that only a small part of this company is maintained active, and the rest is formed with reserve troops, which could be on duty 24 hours after an alert is raised.

Operations at high altitudes
This member of the Escuadrilla de Apoyo al Despliegue Aéreo (EADA) of the Spanish Air Force shows the uniform and equipment necessary for jumps from high altitudes in which one must withstand extremely cold temperatures and use oxygen to breathe.

Portugal has a long tradition of deploying special operations units in places like their former colonies in Africa, Angola and Mozambique, to carry out a wide variety of missions. This tradition has left its mark on the last several decades, and since the deployment of 66 special operations units in June 1998 to rescue civilians caught up in the civil war in Guinea Bissau, it has become the basis for future changes.

For the most part, the men that make up the special forces have come from the army since the reduction and reorganization of its soldiers over the last few years. The Navy also maintains a small group that specializes in combat support missions in the water.

The CIOE

A special operations training center (CIOE) in Lamego is the birthplace of these forces and is headed by a colonel. The school opened its doors on April 16, 1960 with the mission of instructing offi-

International maneuvers
Members of the Portuguese special units participate in exercises in other countries as well as on their own territories in order to share experiences with similar groups.

cers from the army command in various types of special operations. It was also in charge of training sub-units such as the Special Search Companies, some of the Commando Companies that were active in Angola, Mozambique and Guinea and another 12,000 officials and sergeants from other combat units.

Specific missions

The mission of the CIOE covers three areas: training and doctrine, operations and support. Training is administrated by the center with

Modern armaments
The special units of the Portuguese Army have recently received more powerful weapons such as the Sig Sauer P228 pistol and the MP5 automatic rifle, both with a caliber of 9x19 mm Parabellum.

Tough and resistant
Portuguese commandos are in excellent physical condition and are well adapted to operating in the mountains without much external assistance.

courses such as Special Operations with phases in specialization and qualification, Irregular Operations and Commandos. It also carries out studies on doctrine as it relates to the Special Operations units and Irregular Forces. In the area of operations, it participates in assigned missions, both on a national and international level and, if necessary, provides support for civilian protection units.

The center is made up of a Command, Command Company, Training Battalion and Special Operations Association. The Battalion is responsible for the various courses, while the Association groups together sub-units to be used on an operational level in

Preparing for a mission
Loaded down with a heavy backpack and with his personal weapon attached to his body, this Portuguese commando has completed a NATO exercise and waits to be picked up by the plane that will transport him from Rota to Lamego.

direct action, offensive and reconnaissance missions or for indirect actions. On January 1, 1997, the Detachment of Large Radius of Action Patrols, which is part of the Allied Command Europe Mobile Force (AMF) of NATO, was also integrated into these special operations forces available on an operational level.

High level training
The Special Operations course

begins with physical fitness and medical exams looking to select soldiers with team spirit, physical resistance, courage, initiative, self-control and the technical capacities fundamental to succeed in this type of training. Instruction includes armaments and shooting, topography, explosives, communications, hand to hand combat, survival, mountains, aquatic navigation and combat tactics. It takes place in a variety of different arenas both during the day and at night. The training varies according to who it is intended for –officers from the permanent command, volunteer or contracted officers or corporals and soldiers from different recruitment centers. All those who succeed receive a green beret in the final ceremony. The Commandos course,

which began in August 1996, is designed to train commanding officers from those African countries where Portuguese is the official language (PALOP's).

The CIOE also offers specialization courses such as Mountains, Sniper, Survival, Psychological Operations and Large Radius of Action Reconnaissance Patrols. These are rounded off with courses in Parachuting or training periods in Germany for special reconnaissance, Brazil for jungle warfare or Spain to attend the Escuela

Monument to casualties of war
This somber monument on the base at Lamego honors all those who died in combat or during the harsh training sessions which give these forces their special capabilities.

Militar de Montaña y Operaciones Especiales in Jaca. Trainees may also go to the United States to participate in one of the courses run by the U.S. Special Forces or to France or Norway to observe how the extreme cold affects com-

Patrol
These five men make up a special reconnaissance patrol charged with infiltrating enemy lines to observe some vital point and transmit their findings back to the base camp via a radio link.

bat maneuvers.

During multinational exercises such as Strong Resolve, which took place in 1998, or bilateral ones like FORCESGOE, in which Spain and the United States participated, the commanding officers of the CIOE work as a Special Forces Command to support the various simulated missions.

Advanced structure
The Portuguese Commandos, also known as Rangers because one of their first specializations was

obtained through training with these U.S. forces, are part of a Special Operations Battalion (BEOE), which has been merged with the CIOE for structural reasons. The battalion is split into companies (CEOE) with five patrols (PEOE) of thirty men in each. PEOE's are then broken down into groups (GEOE) of twelve soldiers.

In addition, there is the detachment that specializes in reconnaissance patrols and the training staff of the center. Both of these groups could be mobilized together with various reserve companies and former members of special operations units.

Special equipment

As is the case with other sections of the Portuguese Armed Forces, the equipment assigned to these

COMBAT BACKPACK

Members of the special forces are normally deployed in a variety of training zones with everything they need to carry out their assigned exercise. For this reason, they complete their tactical maneuvers with large packs in which they transport all the necessary personal and group equipment: changes of underclothes, coats, combat rations and high-energy food, a thermal mat, climbing equipment, water, a first aid kit, ropes for overcoming obstacles and uneven ground and a long list of things for personal use. For combat support missions, they transport

changes of batteries for the radio, munitions for group weapons, explosives and detonators, materials for the sappers, collapsible communications antennas and observation and orientation equipment.

All of this weighs about 110 pounds, not including equipment for personal protection and individual weapons. This heavy weight restricts movement to a certain extent and makes it necessary to stop quite often to rest during long marches over arid or mountainous terrain.

Harsh conditions
The lifestyle of the members of special units is tough and demands a constant effort to carry out deployments and assigned missions, which generally take place in hostile territories with a lack of resources for survival.

units is gradually improving as a result of the application of new economic proposals for increasing military expenditures.

The collection of uniforms is extensive and of high quality. Camouflage uniforms are based on the British model in terms of production and design. The accessories have also been adapted –belts made of synthetic materials for carrying short arms, large backpacks for transporting equipment to patrols and tactical vests worn by the soldiers who participated in the peace missions in Bosnia.

For protecting the head, a metal helmet based on the U.S M1 model was used until very recently, but it has now been replaced with one made by Kevlar that protects against projectiles and shrapnel. During simulated missions, soldiers also use wide brim hats, wool hats or bandanas tied around

their heads, but reserve the characteristic green beret for other military activities.

Their collection of personal armaments is being renovated, and the fleet of vehicles, which is mostly composed of light four-wheel-drive models, is also in the process of being updated. They have already received the new Sig Sauer P228 pistols rechambered for 9x19 mm Parabellum, and other personal weapons include G3A3/A4 7.62x51 assault rifles (manufactured by permission in Portugal by INDEP) and Heckler und Köck MP5SD6 9 mm automatic rifles with silencer and

Green beret
Portuguese Rangers can be distinguished from other special forces because they wear a green beret with their unit's insignia and another Special Operations badge on their upper arm.

retractable butt.

During combat support missions, the weapons used are normally MG-52 7.62 mm medium machine guns and 60 mm light mortar, which are complemented with disposable rocket launchers for missions that require highly destructive firepower. Explosives, grenades and Accuracy high precision rifles round off the weapons collection. In a short while, it will also include a new 5.56 mm assault rifle, manufactured by the Austrian firm AUG and winner of a contest that took place in the mid-1990's.

Group materials include skiing and climbing equipment, various models of pneumatic vessels and kayaks, outboard motors for powering motor-boats, night vision

viewfinders and portable thermographic equipment capable of locating a man several miles away by the body heat he emits.

Special missions

In Portugal, there are also other units capable of carrying out combat missions designated as special. At the beginning of 1994, the former para-trooper units of the Air Force and the Commandos Army Regiment were integrated into an Airborne Troops (CTAT) Commando Unit in the Tanks section of the Army.

As a result of this union, an Independent Airborne Brigade (BAI) was formed and quartered with the CTAT. It is configured by two infantry battalions and supported by Artillery, Engineer, Service Support, Reconnaissance and Anti-tank units. Its infantrymen receive special training in urban combat, parachuting and special techniques. Their weapons are special as well: Kevlar helmets, Chenowth rapid attack vehicles,

Automatic parachute jump
Two commandos revise their parachuting equipment before a jump. They must check the condition of the chute, the hook that connects it to the paratrooper and review all the safety measures.

Israeli armaments configured by Mini-Uzi 9x19 mm machine gun pistols and AR/ARM 5.56x45 mm assault rifles, Accuracy L96A1 7.62x51 mm high precision rifles and 40 mm automatic grenade launchers made in the United States.

Decree n° 196/85, made on June 25th, called for the formation of a Special Operations Detachment (DAE) within the Continental Riflemen Force, itself part of the Marines of the Portuguese Navy. The missions assigned to this small force of elite specialists include reconnaissance, sabotage, destruction of targets, water raids, assault and destruction of boats and oil rigs and anything else the Navy orders them to do.

To accomplish these missions, soldiers receive specific training in diving and combat swimming, firing weapons, destroying and laying mines, disactivating explosives and air-ground maneuvering with helicopters. They also practice self-defense, advanced lifesaving, orientation and navigation on the ground, driving vehicles, parachuting, surviving by escape and evasion, ground tactics and navigating all types of vessels. These Navy commandos normally train with other similar units, and they have a close relationship with the Spanish Unidad de Operaciones Especiales (UOE) with which they have participated in simulations of emergency evacuations from submarines.

Shooting exercises
In order to ensure that these men are qualified to use the weapons available to them, they pratice on shooting circuits where they must rapidly destroy various targets while constantly reloading their wapons.

The type of missions assigned to special operations units often require they be deployed by air in difficult weather conditions or at night. The helicopter is best suited to this type of flight as it is capable of moving rapidly and close to the ground, thus avoiding detection, to transport small groups of men to their target position (insertion) and pick them up (extraction) when they have completed their mission.

The difficulties inherent in flying several hundred miles per hour only a few feet above the ground require the use of machines specially adapted physically and technologically to the task. It also demands that crew members be well trained in techniques such as LLF (Low Level Flight), which requires an excellent knowledge of the terrain, CF (Contour Flight), which follows the undulations of the terrain to stay low and out of range of enemy radar and NOE (Nap of the Earth), a difficult tech-

The best machine
The Sikorsky SH-60 Black Hawk helicopter is known throughout the world as the leader in its category because it can carry out insertions by flying very close to the ground and provide firepower support to the men it is transporting.

nique involving the disembarkation of commandos in the treetops.

Special techniques

Whether or not they belong to specialized support units for commando groups from different armies, helicopter crew members, usually composed of two pilots and a flight mechanic, should be familiar with the operational requirements necessary for deploying troops from special units. These include the following special tactics in using the aircraft or deploying the men: CSAR, TRAP, fast rope, spy-rig and helocasting.

Rescues in hostile territory
CSAR stands for Combat Search and Rescue and involves

Fast-rope
This is an insertion technique using a thick rope attached to the helicopter. The men slide down it wearing gloves to protect their hands from rope burn and are able to reach the ground safely and rapidly.

carrying out rescue missions in combat zones where there is little chance of encountering the enemy. The person or persons to be rescued (generally the pilot of a search team or the crew members of a helicopter) activate a transmitter which produces a coded pulse that helps the search team to locate them. The search team travels to the zone in one or two helicopters. The first is responsible for placing the rescue team on the ground, while the second covers its position with weapons and acts as a reserve to ensure the success of the mission. Both helicopters are protected by air patrols, and the entire process is coordinated by command planes such as the AWAC's used by NATO.

TRAP (Tactical Recovery of Aircraft and/or Personnel) missions, whose handbooks and parameters of action have been developed by the U.S. Navy, are tactical rescue missions similar to CSAR actions. The difference is that the people being rescued in TRAP missions, such as isolated soldiers in need of assistance,

Very useful

Transport helicopters are platforms that offer a wide variety of uses when supporting the actions of special commando troops, and every country uses them on a regular basis.

and/or the rescue team could be faced with enemy threats.

This type of mission requires the presence of a highly capable combat force, which is deployed as rapidly as possible, before the enemy can react, using many helicopters and fighter planes. A good example of this is the liberation of Captain O'Grady, shot down some years ago while flying in his F-16 over Bosnia. His rescue involved the participation of a hundred commandos, several dozen airplanes and a command ship from the U.S. Navy, which coordinated the mission.

During TRAP actions, personnel may also be deployed to repair a helicopter having problems with one of its vital systems. This involves transporting and protect-

ing the technical personnel charged with the repairs or programming the destruction of the vulnerable systems of a fighter plane or attack plane that has crashed in enemy territory. It may be better to send a team to destroy a F-117 fighter plane or B-2 bomber so that none of its technology can be investigated by other countries looking for its vulnerable points.

Vertical movements

The fast-rope method, or FAST Rope Insertion/Extraction System (FRIES), transports men to a position on the ground where a helicopter cannot land. This may be the deck of a boat, the top of a submarine, a clearing in a forest or the tower of a building.

Boarding

This group of commandos heads toward a SH-3D Sea King helicopter that will be used during a naval assault exercise. This machine has a large cargo capacity and an excellent radius of action.

FIREPOWER SUPPORT

The types of missions carried out by commandos demand that the helicopters that transport them be capable of providing them with firepower support using various weapons such as machine guns, multi-barreled guns, automatic grenade launchers and rocket launchers. These weapons systems can also be used for self-defense from shots fired by enemy groups located in the zone.

These weapons, such as the MiniGun system pictured in the photo, are capable of firing up to 4,000 shots of 7.62x51 mm caliber per minute thanks to their revolving multi-barreled guns. They provide the transported troops with cover and tend to be operated by the flight crew. During CSAR and TRAP rescue missions of pilots or troops shot down in enemy territory, it is very useful to have additional firepower to counteract the maneuvers of enemy troops on the ground so that the captive soldier can be found and removed from the zone.

Soldiers descend via a thick rope running from the cockpit to the ground. The commandos, protected from rope burn by thick gloves and using their feet to slow down, are able to reach the ground rapidly and easily. The problem is that the length of the rope cannot normally exceed thirty to fifty feet, and there are no safety measures if someone falls. For this reason, it is necessary to go through an intensive training process and always follow the proper procedure, such as the use of gloves, when climbing down the rope.

spy-rig is a method used for the rapid extraction of men from a place where a helicopter cannot land, either because of the physical features of the land or for tactical reasons. The soldiers to be rescued put on a harness with a karabiner that attaches to a rope joining the

Assault on oil rigs
Members of the Dutch BBE special group often train in assaulting oil rigs, which would need to be liberated in the case of terrorist capture.

group together. At a time coordinated by radio or illuminated signals, the helicopter approaches the position and lets a cable attached to the fuselage drop down. At the end of the cable there is an element that attaches quickly to the cord joining the men together, and upon receiving the signal, the helicopter commander engages the rotor and lifts them up into the air. The helicopter lands as soon as it is feasible, and all the men transfer into the interior.

Helocasting consists of transporting a group of men, and sometimes their pneumatic vessels and support equipment, to a drop off point in the sea or on a river or marsh. From a safe height of twenty to thirty feet and in stationary flight or at a very slow speed, the men jump into the water in a vertical position to minimize the impact with the water.

The danger with this technique is that if the helicopter is flying too quickly or too high, the men will rebound when impacting with the water and injure themselves. The operation is also limited if the water is swampy with a lot of mud on the bottom as it will be more difficult for the men to reach the surface after jumping.

A variety of activities
The techniques described above are very specific and require a high level of cooperation between the flight crew and the transported personnel, which is only achieved through many joint exercises and simulations. In addition, there are

Launch
CH-47 Chinook heavy transport helicopters are very useful for transporting divers and their pneumatic vessels to the point where they will begin their missions, at which point the men jump into the water and throw in the launches.

other less specific missions that require the collaboration between commandos and helicopters.

Air deployment

The transport of soldiers or specific equipment for use in special missions is very similar to other collaborations between airplanes and ground forces. It is imperative that these types of maneuvers be carried out quietly so as not to raise suspicions about the type of activity in process.

The helicopter has many possibilities as a launch pad; it can be used for parachute jumps over land or sea. Whether the jump is with an automatic or manual chute depends on the qualifications of the paratroopers and the size of the helicopter cabin —an automatic jump requires more room to fix the

Helocasting
This is a technique used to jump from helicopters into the water. It requires total coordination between the height and speed of the machine and the divers so as to avoid any accidents during the jump.

cables to the activators that open the chute, while a manual jump only needs a side door from which the paratroopers jump into space one after the other.

Air forces can also give cover to ground maneuvers during a special mission. For this type of activity, rocket launchers and multiple machine guns are a very useful mean of protecting troops with-

drawing toward the point of extraction under constant harassment from enemy troops and vehicles. In addition, they can destroy enemy facilities during a neutralization mission or the capture of highly valuable prisoners being carried out by the green berets. Finally, they can provide air cover during a NEO (Non-Combatant Evacuation Operation).

Some missions require that troops be transported to the point of initiation of the activity or to vessels on which it is impossible to land. In these cases, soldiers can rappel down to the ground by using a harness to slide down one or several ropes running from the cockpit of the helicopter. In order

to facilitate their descent, a man at the bottom advises them on each movement. For rappelling it is better to break in the rope first because the new ones stick to the person descending and can cause pulled muscles. Soldiers practice this maneuver during NATO exercises in which they must jump about 400 feet.

They may also use ladders made of metal cable to reach the ground. In this case, it is better if someone can hold the ladder at the bottom so it doesn't sway. This technique is used by the U.S. Rangers, who drop a ladder out the door of their CH-47 Chinook helicopters so that a group of twenty men can deploy to the ground in little more than a minute.

Disembarkation
These Portuguese commando troops have been transported by an Alouette III helicopter to a position from which the men will parachute to the ground to initiate their mission.

Ladders may also be used to pick up green berets after a mission. The men can easily climb up the ladder as long as they are not loaded down with their heavy packs and armaments which can, of course, limit their movements.

Adapted models
In order to complete the activities previously mentioned, standard helicopters as well as models specially modified to support special forces are used. One modified helicopter is the new Eurocopter

Ground crew
Some members of commando groups are specially trained to act as ground crew and direct the landing maneuvers of the helicopters which support their missions. They give instructions to the pilot with arm movements.

AS 532 A2 Cougar RESCO, which has been purchased by the French Air Force to rescue pilots shot down in enemy territory. For this purpose, it has millimeter radar for tracking objects on the ground, a FLIR infrared tracking system for night use, a perch that is used to refuel the machine during flight so as to increase its range and powerful engines with exhaust tubes facing up to avoid heat sensitive enemy missiles. The Cougar is also equipped with extra armor plating on various parts of its fuselage and stands for attaching different types of weapons.

Another specialized model is the U.S helicopter Sikorsky MH-60K, based on the economical design of the UH-60 Black Hawk. The model used by U.S special forces includes several half wings on the upper section of the fuselage for holding additional fuel tanks and a perch for refueling during flight. It also has a Hughes AN/AAQ-16 infrared tracker, a Texas Instruments AN/APQ-174A ground tracker, counter measure launchers and stands for Stinger air missiles. It can carry up to ten fully equipped men –the same capacity as the HH-60G Pave Hawk used by the U.S Air Force for rescuing their pilots.

Rescue missions can also be carried out by some MH-53J Pave Low III models, based on the Sikorsky Super Stallion. These helicopters have a large capacity and were used (in smaller models) with great success during the Vietnam War and in 1979 in Operation Eagle Claw to liberate a group of Americans being held in Iran. The newer model is equipped with V-22 Osprey variable wings designated as CV-22B by USSOCOM. This model can turn its rotors to land and rise in a vertical position or use them in a normal position for a larger radius of action and a higher speed.

Other countries with more limited budgets have to introduce small

ANVIS NIGHT VISION GOGGLES

AN/AVS-6 ANVIS

Helicopter pilots assigned to special transport missions normally carry out their missions at night to avoid being seen. Night flights require the use of night vision systems that are generally attached to the crews' helmets. One of the better known models is the ANVIS (Aviator's Night Vision Imaging System) AN/AVS-6 manufactured by the U.S firm ITT Defense & Electronics at their factory in Roanoke.

It is composed of a helmet attachment and a binocular module, which goes in front of the pilot's eyes. The binoculars have two sensor tubes, which in the most recent models correspond to the OMNIBUS IV generation known for their improved resolution and amplification. The entire apparatus weighs 21 ounces and can be used for a total of 10,000 hours (compared with 2,000 hours for earlier models).

The system may be operated in temperatures ranging from -25°F to +125°F and uses alkaline or lithium batteries with three volts. The focus can be adjusted from 10 inches to infinity, and it can be modified from +2 to –6 diopters depending on the graduation of the operator's vision.

changes in the transport models they already have in their helicopter fleets. These models include the powerful U.S. Chinook, which is sold all over the world and is known as a very capable machine, and the Westland Sea King, used by the British until the new EH-101 Merlin is available and can be transformed to fulfill specific requirements. Another adaptable model is the Russian MIL Mi-8, transformed with additional armor plating, elements for lowering troops to the ground and floats for landing in calm waters.

Helicopters that can be useful for combat missions include the different variants of the Aérospatiale/Westland SA 330 Puma and the more advanced

Difficult conditions
UH-1H Iroquois helicopters continue to be used by many countries all over the world and are capable of transporting special groups to the most remote areas, including ice-covered mountain tops.

Super Puma or derivations of the Bell UH-1 Iroquois such as the AB-412 and those made by the Italian company Agusta. In addition, small models such as the Westland Lynx can be used by naval assault groups to get at to hard to reach areas like oil rigs or vertical refueling points on various types of ships.

Classic method
Rappelling is also a method used by soldiers to reach the ground from helicopters. Commandos attach a harness to a rope and safely slide down to the ground.

THE DUTCH GREEN BERETS

Holland may be a small European country, but it has a lot of economic power and its former colonies support its military capacity. The Dutch government has made a great effort to maintain an armed forces that is very powerful and well-equipped with modern systems and advanced technology. It is actively involved in NATO and maintains various alliances with countries such as Great Britain, with which it has a joint Navy Brigade, and Spain, with which it produces various types of ships. Government policy has also made it possible to sustain small groups, under the command of the army or the navy, capable of carrying out special operations and counter terrorist actions.

Anywhere
These troops are trained to maneuver and fight on the most difficult terrain, and they are qualified to combat all types of enemy forces.

Special ground operations

These types of missions are the responsibility of a select group of soldiers in the Dutch Army called the Korps Commando Troepen (KCT). This unit dates back to various commando raids carried out in 1942 during the Second World War.

Organically structured

The close to four hundred soldiers currently involved in the KCT are organized into a command unit, a SIC group and Companies 104, 105 and 108, which have nine squads for a total of 34 teams of eight men each. Each squad has eight teams with the same configuration: a commanding lieutenant, five specialized sergeants and two corporals.

Of these men, two are specialized in using LTD (Laser Target

Constant exercises
This high tower is the scene of various exercises in vertical maneuvering such as rappelling. This photo shows a simulation of rappelling down from a transport helicopter.

Their training process follows a plan perfectly adapted to the type of missions they are responsible for and the type of terrain on which they are deployed. Almost four and a half years are necessary to train an individual in the variety of required specialties.

The first phase in training is BMT (Basic Military Training), which lasts a little more than two months and enables the soldiers to strengthen their physical capacities, learn the basic skills associated with using armaments and military equipment and become familiar with the first specialized courses. The next phase is BCT (Basic Commando Training), which is fourteen weeks of physical and mental hardening in the form of marches, all types of exercises, tests of bravery, practice on difficult terrain and other subjects. If they pass, the soldiers move on to six months of intensive work in the ACT (Advanced Commando Training) phase.

Designators), which illuminate targets so they can be hit by high precision weapons launched from the air or ground. Another two men can set up and maneuver the communications systems, and two others are qualified in medicine and in charge of administering first aid to their fellow soldiers if the need arises. Another pair are experts in the use of explosives and detonators, and the final two are select marksmen whose capacities are hidden by their unit so they can perform a wide range of activities in combat.

The teams of each company are qualified to carry out insertions with vehicles, helicopters or on foot, but there are also teams specialized in water insertions and maneuvers. Other teams are trained in HALO and HAHO parachuting techniques using oxygen tanks, and still others possess the techniques necessary to maneuver

Different training process
These units of the Dutch special forces normally train in an area of Britain to qualify in urban combat. This is why they are using SA80 rifles, although they don't form a part of their usual assigned equipment.

over mountains and other types of difficult terrain.

The SIC includes Logistical, Communications, Security and Training squads. This last group contains personnel specialized in intelligence, weapons, water, demolitions, survival, parachuting, communications, mountains, tactics, outdoor training and command training.

Within the SIG, the *305 Commando Troepen Batalijon* is a group of commando reserves who are available for service if necessary.

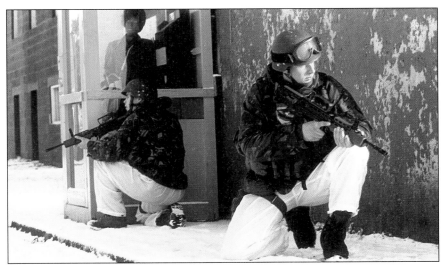

This 26 week period involves training in demolitions, first aid, high precision shooting, automatic parachuting, patrol maneuvers, concealment and deep reconnaissance actions. Upon completing the first year of training, the men are capable of performing special operations with a relatively high success rate. Three more years are necessary for more specific training in special reconnaissance, direct actions, counter terrorism missions, diving, designating targets with lasers and other techniques, HALO and HAHO manual parachuting jumps using oxygen and other areas that require a special individual qualification.

To carry out these actions, the men are provided with equipment such as Glock 17 pistols, C7A1 assault rifles and C8A1 carbines with attachments for M203 single-shot grenade launchers and Barrett M82A1 rifles capable of firing .50 caliber munitions. They are also equipped with disposable rocket launchers, FN MAG medium machine guns, Stinger ground to air missile systems and TOW II anti-tank missile systems installed in Mercedes light four-wheel-drive vehicles.

Select marksmen
These teams of military snipers are trained to conceal themselves in a specific part of the terrain, observe enemy movements and accurately hit targets with high tactical value. Then they retreat without any outside help.

Assigned missions

The KCT group is the Dutch unit assigned to special missions, and its organization, equipment, training and C3I structure (Command, Control and Communications) have been developed for these types of actions. The initial selection, with a year long training process, guarantees a force of highly capable individuals with many operational possibilities. The material studied includes all types of specific military operations including counter terrorism actions.

Its general missions include all those that fall under the category of special operations such as providing support for two simultaneous peacekeeping operations with deployments of four teams each and a duration of not more than three years. The KCT

Combat exercises
Members of the Dutch special units are qualified in urban and rural combat. In order to obtain this qualification, they train in all types of situations, including using real firepower.

must also serve as a center for doctrine and guarantee the training of its own men as well as the other groups assigned to support it through combat or administrative services.

All of these missions require personnel specially trained to operate in hostile territories while always maintaining a high level of command so as to follow proper procedure. Active or passive actions follow those guidelines established in the AJP-A published by NATO: special reconnaissance, direct actions, military assistance and group company activities.

Special reconnaissance missions involve obtaining specific data on important operational or strategic targets. They are usually carried out prior to the advance of conventional troops so as to locate military and non-military targets, obtain precise information on the deployment area or watch over highly valuable installations in enemy territory.

Direct actions include attacks on very important targets that must be

Varied missions
These commando groups can carry out reconnaissance missions or direct actions like destroying enemy equipment or capturing valuable enemy personnel.

destroyed or disabled, sabotaging enemy communication lines, neutraliz-

ing specific equipment like radar or communications centers, capturing or eliminating important enemy personnel and evacuating troops. At the moment, the Dutch do not participate in missions of military assistance to other countries. They are limited to their own troops including CSAR (Combat Search and Rescue) units, which are responsible for dealing with international terrorism, organized crime and drug trafficking, and those units that provide support during disasters and natural catastrophes.

They have also been responsible for peace-keeping missions in support of the Dutch contingent deployed in Bosnia between 1995 and 1998 and in Kosovo in 1999. Finally, they have helped to evacuate Dutch personnel from other countries that have gotten caught up in dangerous situations or civil war there.

Peace-keeping operation
The Dutch commandos have been deployed in Bosnia as part of the SFOR unit of NATO to carry out missions for peace in the Balkans.

THE DUTCH GREEN BERETS

Specialized organizations

In addition to the KCT units deployed by the army, there are also other specialized organizations under the command of the military police or the Marine Corps. These units are qualified to carry out special missions on various types of terrain and with many operations possibilities, both in times of peace and times of conflict.

Patrolling the border

The *Koninklijke Marechaussee* is a police unit that is responsible for guarding the border and acting as military police. It also collaborates with other sections of the Dutch police if the need arises. It is composed of two

specialized units: the BBS (*Brigade Speciale Beveiligingsopdrachten*), which carries out surveillance and intelligence missions in support of other protective actions, and the BBEK (*Bijzondere Bijstandseenheid Krijgsmacht*), a SWAT unit of the military police that supports the actions of the armed forces and has the

Naval assault
The men of the BBE are specialized in all types of special operations with various types of naval targets, like oil rigs, under attack by terrorist groups.

Reconnaissance patrol
Weighed down with heavy packs and a sleigh for moving group equipment or an injured soldier, these four members of a reconnaissance patrol travel over the snow toward the area of their assigned mission.

First aid
The training period for special forces includes instruction in dealing with the minor accidents that can happen during exercises or operational deployments.

basic mission of responding to possible terrorist attacks or other attacks on Dutch military installations.

The Marines also have a special unit called the 23rd Airborne Company, or Whiskey Co., which is organized and operates much like the British BPT (Brigade Patrol Group). They are specialists in combat on mountains and arctic areas, reconnaissance, parachuting and insertion with small vessels. In case of a war involving NATO nations, control of this unit would be passed along to the 3rd Commando Brigade in Great Britain.

Bijzondere Bijstands Eenheid
This is the name of the Dutch special assault military unit, which is spe-

cialized in high risk missions or those involving terrorists with hostages. It is known internationally by the initials BBE, and it is composed of about 90 Royal Marines who are selected after a special 48 week training course, which enables them to operate in all types of situations.

In theory, terrorists should be captured alive, but this has not been the case in the missions that have taken place. In June 1977, the BBE simultaneously assaulted a school and a train in which terrorists from the Moluccas had taken two hundred people hostage. In the end, six terrorists were eliminated, and two hostages were also killed. More recently, they been deployed in the Adriatic Sea to enforce the arms embargo against the Serbs, but it is not known if they had to act with force.

Training of BBE's is an ongoing process, and the group includes select marksmen and psychologists specialized in dealing with hostage situations. Their weapons include Colt Lawman .357 Magnum revolvers, Sig-Sauer P226 pistols, MP5 automatic rifles, H&K G3MSG assault rifles and Steyr SSG high precision rifles. They are also equipped with four-wheel-drive vehicles, launches and transport helicopters. The BBE operative base is located in Rotterdam, but there is always a detachment on the Soesterberg air base in case the police request their deployment.

Sophisticated equipment
The equipment available to these troops is varied and modern and includes compact C8A1 assault rifles with global position systems to ensure incredible accuracy.

I n 1992, following in the footsteps of the United States and Great Britain some years earlier, the French formed their own special operations command –the COS (*Commandement des Opérations Spéciales*). This action grouped together a considerable force of commandos specialized in many types of missions. The military unit, with ample possibilities for resolving all kinds of crises, has provided the Parisian government with an easily deployable element to support French interests either in helping ally regimes or maintaining a presence in the most controversial parts of the world.

Quality equipment
This French soldier, waiting to board a transport plane and parachute down to the ground, shows some examples of his equipment and armaments like this Swiss Sig-Sauer 551 assault rifle with retractable butt.

A demonstrated need
The initial task of putting all the French special forces under one command was assigned to General Maurice Le Page, who carried out preliminary studies in 1991 and the beginning of 1992. The constitution of the COS was approved on August 1, 1992, and the general was named

Advanced communications
The portable equipment used by the French includes systems like this one, which uses a collapsible antenna to connect to faraway points via coded links offered by satellites in orbit around the earth.

the first head of the joint command, a post he held until April 1996 when he was replaced by another general. The job rotates between representatives from l'Armée de Terre, la Marine Nationale and l'Armée de l'Air.

Operational organization
The COS is made up of 1,500 members of the French special operations units, not including the crew of helicopters and transport planes assigned to tactical and strategic transports. The headquarters is composed of fifty men, divided between the Taverny barracks

Day or night
The increased use of night vision equipment, like the compact goggles worn by this soldier, and visible and infrared laser prompters is especially helpful when planning interventions in adversely lit conditions.

and the Ministry of Defense in Paris, who are under the direct command of the CEMA (*Chief d'État-Major des Armées*).

The Chief of the Joint General Staff is assisted by his own General Staff Head, who acts as the second in command and coordinates the activities of the officers, junior officers and troops at Taverny. The CEMA is also aided by the personnel in charge of managing satellite links, a GSIGN liaison with the gendarme and a medical officer responsible for coordinating health services during training courses. In addition, he counts on army, marine and air force attachés to coordinate petitions regarding ships, planes and other elements necessary for planned missions.

These personnel and other soldiers are integrated into the following units: Operations, Specialized Training, Research and Development, Telecommunications and Information Systems, Civilian and Military Actions and General Services. The Specialized Training unit is responsible for analyzing all the information and intelligence available and planning the necessary training activities including obtaining the required authorizations for deployments, working with the other departments and coordinating the maneuvers and exchanges of personnel in exercises with countries like Morocco, Oman and Tunisia.

Investigation and Development is in charge of finding the new equipment necessary for the missions and evaluating the techniques associated with it. Computers and sophisticated communications systems are the materials used by the Telecommunications and Information Systems unit. Civilian Actions coordinates local information and restricts information about combat by using a team of reserves specialized in public relations or the economy, and General Services guarantees the proper functioning of the COS via administrative and financial services.

The inner circle
This is composed of highly trained units available at a moment's notice for operational use. The group is fronted by the 1° Régiment Parachutiste d'Infanterie de Marine (RPIMA) based in Bayonne and descended from the paratrooper units formed by the

Constant training
The soldiers of special units, like this member of the 13th Regiment of Dragoon Paratroopers, are better qualified than other soldiers because they spend a lot of time in training and exercises.

Tactical vest
This tactical vest is one of the new wardrobe items assigned to French units. It can comfortably transport clips and compact first aid kits thanks to its numerous pockets.

Special Air Service during the Second World War. Its mission is to obtain strategic intelligence information and carry out direct actions behind enemy lines.

The participation of the RPIMA in direct actions led to its inclusion in the 11th Airborne Division of the FAR (*Force d'Action Rapide*) until it was integrated into the COS as part of the *Groupement Spécial Autonome* (GSA). This regiment is structured to include a headquarters, a training company, a communications team and three combat RAPAS (*Recherche at Action Spécialisée*) teams, which carry out actions during specific operations.

The first RAPAS is specialized in direct actions in urban environ-

ments, activities in the water and providing security for dignitaries. The second is an urban warfare group with specializations in explosives, sabotage, controlling access to vulnerable points and sniper missions. The third combat team is provided with equipment for deep reconnaissance, like high mobility four-wheel-drive vehicles, and for firepower support, like heavy mortar and anti-air missile systems. This division of specializations

means that the best unit is chosen for each mission. Then combat teams are formed of 150 to 160 men configured in squadrons (the operational center of the regiment) of ten soldiers each: an experienced officer in charge of the command unit including the team leaders, a radio operator, a communications specialist, a doctor and three teams of two men specialized in areas like sabotage, controlling access points, the fast rope method, high precision shooting and maneuvering over difficult terrain.

The headquarters includes three GCP (*Groupement de Commandos Parachutiste*) who participate in LRP (Long Range Patrol) deep

Attack vehicles
The company ACMAT has supplied the French special operations units with these light trucks modified with various stands for all types of weapons and designed to operate in enemy territory during direct actions or reconnaissance missions.

THERMAL CAMERA

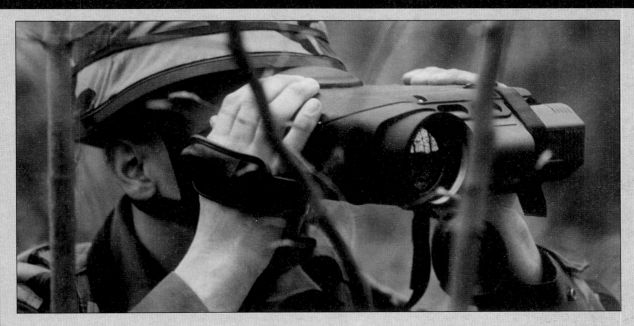

Thompson CSF Optronique, a French company with its factory in Guyancourt, manufactures various observation materials including these modern Sophie binoculars that can be used in temperatures ranging from -27°F to +131°F. This system, which includes an electronic mode for increasing the size of the area being watched, is composed of a lightweight module weighing 5.3 pounds and with dimensions of 10x4x12 inches. It also includes a front monocle associated with some optronic elements that make it possible to locate a person by their body heat at a distance of 1.25 miles or a vehicle or an airplane up to 3.75 miles away; this can be done during the day or at night.

Its advantage over other systems is that it is very comfortable to carry, and it can be used for 4 hours thanks to its rechargeable battery. In addition, no previous training is required to use it, and it is very useful for special forces who normally have to carry heavy equipment which is expensive and prone to breakdowns. It comes with connections for hooking it up to a video recorder and a video communications system with a high frequency radio link.

reconnaissance actions and are qualified in HALO and HAHO manual parachute jumps using oxygen tanks. Many of them are also capable of doing tandem jumps in which two people share a chute. Working alongside this group is the Intelligence Unit, which manages information from many countries and armies and is responsible for regimental training.

Selecting men and equipment

30% of the COS is composed of officers and junior officers, while the remaining troops are chosen through a rigorous selection process that only 50% of the candidates pass. The selection process includes an initial phase of two months dedicated to basic topics and another seven months of commando training. Service with the unit lasts three years and includes more specific training periods like a 15 month advanced commando course. Troops regularly train in the jungles of Guyana, the Djibouti desert and urban combat installations in Pau. Some members are also qualified in combat swimming by the Valbonne Diving School.

Special uniforms and accessories are available to facilitate movements during urban combat. Weapons include Smith & Wesson 656 revolvers, Mini-Uzi and MP5 automatic rifles, Mossberg and Benelli M-3 shotguns and 5.56 assault rifles like the Famas with a Trijicon ACOG viewfinder or the

M16 with a M-203 single-shot grenade launcher. In addition, there are G3 7.62 assault rifles and high precision rifles such as the MSG-90 and Ultima Ratio Commando II with a caliber of .308 Winchester and Barrett M-82A1 and Hecate II with a caliber of .50 Browning.

More powerful weapons include Minimi light machine guns and M2 heavy ones, MGL grenade launchers from South Africa and GMG automatic ones made by Germany, 60 mm mortars like the Vektor, Stinger and Mistral anti-air missile launchers and ACMAT VLRA intervention trucks with room for 12 men and various weapons stands. Nocturnal movements are carried out with the assistance of OB-42 or 50 vision systems and Lucie goggles, and communications are assured with a wide range of equipment including

Constant collaboration
The deployments of French special units demand the collaboration of l'Armée de l'Air, which provides the air transport necessary to reach the initial point of the exercise or real operation.

Different areas
The equipment, training, preparation and demonstrated capacity in real operations of the French Special Operations Command puts them among the elite of similar Western forces.

TRC-743 and 745 systems that transmit images and data via Inmmarsat satellites.

Special actions
Another section of the COS is the COFUSCO (*Commandement des Fusiliers Marins Commandos*). It is based at the Lorient Naval Base and is composed of four assault units designated the Jaubert, Trepel, Penfentenyo and Montfort Commando Units. These are all organized the same: 80 soldiers distributed among the ECT (*Element de Commandement et de Transmissions*) for command and communications and units of Reconnaissance, Assault, and Direct Actions/Firepower Support.

Specialized combat
Each of these sections is divided into four squads of 20 men each and then again into two combat teams.

They can be called up very quickly because they have equipment stockpiled on various naval bases. There are teams deployed in Toulon and Djibouti, and they maintain their capacities by training for different situations on the French coast. The equipment they use is special and includes Colt M773 assault rifles with lasers, Beta-Mag clips with 100 cartridges, Sig-Sauer 551 and 40 mm single-shot grenade launchers, MILAN anti-tank missile launchers and LG1 Fly-K 60 mm grenade launchers. They also have the use of Remington 870 bolt action shotguns, Gepard 14.5 mm rifles from Hungary, AJM-DLR laser designators and night vision equipment made by the U.S firm Litton.

Their training includes maneuvering in aquatic environments with Zodiac Hurricane pneumatic vessels powered by two 175 horsepower out board motors or parachuting directly into the sea. The combat divers of the Comando Hubert and the

Prepared for the future

The French have already initiated several programs to improve the capacity of their soldiers to carry out a variety of missions. The process includes modifications in uniforms and protective elements and new weapons.

Groupe de Combat en Milieu Clos (GCMC), also part of the COFUS-CO, are especially well-trained for operating in the water.

French divers, based at Toulon, are divided into two companies, a combat support and an operational company, composed of 50 divers in A, B, C and D squads. The A squad is in command of the section and is equipped with Hurricane and EF launches. B is specialized in counter terrorism maritime activities, C is responsible for underwater operations and D carries out reconnaissance and support missions. The

squads use DC-55 closed circuit diving systems and Vostock NK mini submarines, which can transport two men and 220 pounds of explosives. Some members are also qualified in HALO and HAHO parachute jumps.

The GCMC is a very specialized unit of 17 men trained in anti-terror-

Hard work

Deployments in mountainous zones demand a lot of effort from the type of troops that normally travel on foot over long distances carrying heavy packs. The French use ski poles during these maneuvers.

ist combat actions in maritime environments during which one of the two assault teams is deployed. The men wear navy blue uniforms and bulletproof vests that also serve as life jackets, and they are equipped with thick helmets and armor-plated viewfinders. Their weapons include Sig-Sauer P226 pistols with Sure-Fire spotlight and lasers and MP5SD3 and A5 automatic rifles, with which they can detain anyone attempting to take a civilian or marine vessel.

Another unit included in the COS is the 10th Paratrooper Commando with three squads in Nîmes. It is deployed during missions that require the infiltration of units to carry out reconnaissance activities at great distances from the home base or when it is necessary to capture an enemy air base with French airplanes. Weapons that are useful for these types of missions include WASP light rocket launchers and PR4G communications systems. In addition, the 13th Regiment of Dragoon Paratroopers assists in the obtainment of intelligence.

The helicopters assigned to French commando missions are the Cougar, Puma and Gazelle fleet of the ALAT (*Aviation Légère de l'Armée de Terre*), which are organized into special operations squadrons. The air force provides C-130 Hercules and Transall transport planes from the DOS-CIET.

Operational experience

This special operations command center was only formed a few years ago, but its members already have a wealth of experience. In 1992, units of the RPIMA participated in Operation Osite in the Comores archipelago to stabilize the country after the assassination of President Abdhallah and to confront mercenary troops. In December of that same year, they were active in Operation Oryx in Somalia, which lasted until February 1993. This mission was a mixture of humanitarian aid and military presence and

German armaments
French special operations units, like those in other countries, have adapted the reliable German MP5 automatic rifles in a variant equipped with an integrated silencer and infrared laser designators.

Combat SAR
The French have some Cougar helicopters modified to participate in rescue missions in enemy territory. For this reason, they have refueling perches, optronic systems, weapons attachments and additional armor plating.

involved the deployment of 120 COS troops only five days after they were alerted to the mission.

At the same time this mission was being carried out, another detachment was preparing to participate in Operation Balbuzard in the Adriatic Sea, and other units were deployed to Burundi, the Ivory Coast, Congo, Gabon and Rwanda. Some units also went to Bosnia to help establish a neutral zone around Gorazde and Sarajevo and to help extract a British Special Air Service group. In May 1994, an evacuation of French citizens in Yemen was conducted and troops were also activated for Operation Turquoise in Rwanda. In 1995, units were immersed in Operation Balbuzard in the Adriatic, Operations Nautile I and Nautile II to prevent the actions of the Greenpeace ship Rainbow

Warrior in French waters and Operation Azalée to confront Bob Denard's mercenaries in the Comores islands.

More recently, missions have included rescuing the pilots of a Mirage 2000 fighter-bomber shot down over Bosnia, Operations Almadin 1 and 2 in the Central African Republic, Operation Alba to secure the port of Dürres in Albania and Operations Iroko and Malachite against the militias in Guinea and the Congo. They were also activated in the beginning of 1999 to form part of an extraction team to rescue the NATO pilots attack-ing Serb military colonies.

HIGH PRECISION RIFLES

The French company PGM Precision, specializing in the design and manufacture of rifles with maximum accuracy from large distances, has its headquarters in Poisy. Its range of weapons, used by the French Special Forces and the Navy, includes the Ultima Ratio offered in calibers like .308 Winchester (7.62x51 mm) and .338 Lapua Magnum (8.6x70 mm). This is a bolt action rifle with an ergonomic element that facilitates aiming.

This model, with a standard variant including a 24 inch barrel and weighing 12 pounds, is also offered in a version with an integrated silencer that is very accurate and silent (83 decibels with subsonic munitions). The Commando I and II models are equipped with a short barrel and a retractable butt which shortens their length so that they can be easily transported.

The biggest in the range is the Hecate II with .50 Browning (12,70x99 mm) munitions and a weight of 30 pounds. It is a bolt action rifle, its clips have space for seven cartridges and it is offered with various fittings depending on the needs of the user.

NAVAL BOARDING OPERATIONS

Commando groups are military units specialized in carrying out reconnaissance and direct action missions. This second type of mission involves capturing targets that are highly valuable in terms of military importance or for a variety of other considerations. Among the most common actions, especially since the naval embargos declared a few years ago in the Persian Gulf and the Adriatic Sea, are naval boardings of ships transporting cargo that try to evade the patrols of military forces deployed in the area. Ships may also be boarded for a concrete military benefit such as

Coordinated maneuver
Once one group has arrived by air, the others head for the sides of the ship in pneumatic vessels with powerful out board motors which enable them to arrive at their destination with great speed.

Air assault
The first commando group arrives at the target ship in a helicopter and uses the fast rope technique to reach the deck quickly and safely, without giving the crew time to react or escape.

capturing special weapons or detaining traffickers who get rich off illegally dealing in weapons, drugs or other types of smuggling.

Coordination phase
These missions require a small group that varies in content depending on the type of ship to be assaulted –a slow-moving freighter or a military ship. In general, several teams of six to eight men are used, for a total of twenty commandos.

These soldiers (the photos show members of the special operations

unit of the Spanish Navy during an exercise) must already be familiar with this difficult and specific assault technique. They have spent many hours practicing it to reach the highest level of coordination between the members of the team. The must also be in excellent physical condition and well-

Regrouping

The first assault team regroups at a position on the deck near the landing point to initiate their advance on the vital areas of the target ship. This is a critical moment because they are very vulnerable to enemy attack.

trained in the use of weapons in case the crew must be restrained.

Encircling maneuvers

The type of target determines the manner in which the commando group will reach the deck of the ship. They use a variety of techniques. For example, if the target is a slow-moving supertanker with a high deck or an aircraft carrier, the insertion is carried out from the air by manual parachute so as to land accurately and discreetly, especially at dawn or dusk. The paratroopers leave their parachutes on the deck and act quickly to accomplish the task.

Nevertheless, insertions are usually done with helicopters or sea vessels because they are easily

available, involve less risks to use and can rapidly reach the desired position. Helicopters fly low to the ground until they reach the stern of the ship where they can conceal their presence with the noise of the machine and the superstructures. In this situation, the fast rope technique is used because it is quick and the helicopter can avoid landing on unprepared sections of the deck. The disadvantage with this technique is that the helicopter is very vulnerable to light weapons or portable ground to air missile launchers. Therefore, other aircraft are required to protect the helicopter with machine guns, high precision weapons or rocket launchers.

Assault vessels tend to be semi-rigid and transported to the area on a mother ship or launched out of

Coordinated operation

On the port and starboard sides, commando groups have attached rope ladders, which they climb up with great difficulty as the ship is still moving quickly along. This task requires excellent physical and technical training.

planes using parachutes or the helocasting method. The advantage with this method is that their small size and quiet motors enable them to silently and speedily approach the stern and port side of the ship. The disadvantages are the complications involved with attaching a rope or metallic ladder to the deck and climbing up it, keeping in mind that the two vessels are traveling alongside each other at a certain speed, the conditions of the sea vary according to the area and the combatants are very vulnerable to enemy attack when climbing.

Coordinated assault

To lessen the inconveniences of both methods and take advantage of their benefits, missions are normally organized using both techniques so as to create a safer environment when approaching the designated targets.

Before anything else, a coordination phase deals with information relative to the target and the assigned mission. First, it is necessary to be familiar with the general characteristics of the ship, the flag,

Air coordination
In a small helicopter, the command team travels to coordinate the maneuvers from the air and maintain radio links with the teams deployed on the target ship. Also travelling aboard is a marksman qualified to use a high precision rifle or a light machine gun to cover his fellow soldiers.

the crew and the country of origin. It is also important to discuss the type of cargo being transported and the precautions necessary so it won't be damaged, the maximum speed of the ship, the height of its flanks and any other significant details. Secondly, verifications must be made on the men being deployed, the methods being used, any threats that could be encountered and the plan of attack once the deck of the ship is reached.

With all the data obtained from various intelligence sources, the assault plan is prepared and analyzed and, if possible, a simulation is carried out with a naval unit of similar characteristics.

This refines certain aspects of the operation, better coordinates the movements of the combatants and points out any minor details which might become significant during the mission.

Once having established a plan and practiced it with the soldiers and equipment involved, it is only necessary to wait for the order to initiate the mission. Political conditions can slow down the start of the intervention and have a negative influence on the decisions

Rapid advance
In order to be successful, the mission must be carried out in a short amount of time with a high level of accuracy. This assures that the ship is controlled and avoids confrontations with crew members who have locked themselves in vital areas.

made by the men in charge of the operation.

Taking action against the target

The reports filed say that the target ship has a crew of about thirty men, none of whom have any idea that a BOARDEX (Boarding Exercise) operation is being planned against them to capture the ship and its precious cargo. The cargo could be radioactive materials, produced by one of the former Soviet republics to be sold to a country with aspirations of gaining some importance on the international scene, or chemical products that may be used to manufacture highly dangerous chemical weapons.

Phase 1: Assault

The commandos travel by air until they reach one of their ships or an ally ship that will take them to the zone where the target is located. This naval unit might be in charge of tracking the ship before it is boarded. An amphibious vessel is excellent for this task because of its capacity and

First target

The first group of commandos has arrived at the main bridge where they have detained the crew members who run the ship. At this moment, their control of the ship is significant, and they have completed the first phase of the assault.

operational possibilities.

Once the assault group is established in this position, the last phase of planning is initiated. This includes how the maneuvers will be carried out and what methods will be used. A possible combination is the use of two heavy transport helicopters and one light one, which can be deployed simultaneously to the landing zone of the amphibious vessels at the stern of the ship. One of the heavy helicopters will be used for transporting the first team, designated "Tango", and the other will carry the soldiers in charge of using special weapons to provide cover for the operation.

The pneumatic vessels may be operated from the unsinkable dike that characterizes navy ships, or they can be dropped in the water with the cranes that military ships have on their decks. They should be semi-rigid pneumatic vessels that are lightweight and have excellent nautical qualities. In addition,

Precise movements

Maneuvering around ladders, decks, hallways and the other twists and turns of a ship is not an easy task because they are narrow spaces that are often slippery or steep. For this reason, the commandos should be agile and wear tactical boots prepared for the situation.

they should be powered by two powerful out board motors that can reach speeds of up to forty knots.

During the operation, at least three launches should be provided for the "Papa" group, boarding on the port side, one for the "Sierra" group, boarding on the starboard and another one reserved to provide cover for the others and rescue the men that fall into the water during the initial contact phase.

To assure they are taken by surprise, the naval maneuvers should begin one or two hours before sunrise. The helicopters should move just before the first rays of sun start to shine, when the pilots can fly in the increasing light without night vision goggles.

When the target ship is near, the insertion crew should slow down their speed and approach the stern as is it more difficult to be seen there. The helicopter carrying the "Tango" group should be the first to arrive because the noise can be used to cover the movements of the men

Machine room

The engine and controls are vital when it comes to capturing a ship, so an assault group is sent to control these machines. They detain the crew members and take charge of the controls in this area.

descending from the air by the fast rope method and the commandos climbing up the sides of the ship by rope ladders attached to the rails.

Phase 2: control

This type of assault requires equipment such as light bullet-proof protection on the chest and head, tactical boots that don't slip on wet decks or greasy interiors, personal communications systems that can be activated without hands for constant links with the exterior and light armaments like

pistols and automatic rifles for confronting armed threats. The men providing cover from the helicopter use assault rifles with telescopic attachments or light and medium machine guns to force the

ship and its crew to desist.

The "Tango" team, which has been the first to board, divides into two groups and heads for the bridge by each of the gunwales. Meanwhile, the "Papa" and "Sierra" teams target the machine room and the cabins where, at this hour, most of the crew are probably sleeping. In order to gain control of the ship, the machine room is vital, and it is a good idea if some of the commandos understand the

A calm moment

One of the commando officers is maintaining radio contact with the command group in charge of coordinating the action, while his men control the bridge. Another two groups are working below deck to control the rest of the vital areas.

Finished operation
When all the crew members have been captured or neutralized, the dangerous cargo has been verified and the command center has been informed of the outcome of the mission, the soldiers take up their guard positions and maneuver the ship back to port.

After searching the ship from top to bottom and establishing guard positions, the commandos will contact the command by radio link to inform them of the success of the mission. Then they will return to a friendly port where the captured crew will be taken away and, using any necessary technical means, the cargo will be unloaded and the dangerous materials disactivated.

This type of operation is a good example of the operational possibilities of commando groups, both in times of war or in crisis situations.

how to run it so that they can maneuver the boat back to the port when the mission is finished.

All the members of the crew should be handcuffed. The commandos normally use thick plastic cuffs as they are easy to carry and very resistant. The entire crew, except the captain who will be interrogated about the cargo, will be imprisoned in a room guarded by the special units. In addition, the contents of the cargo should be verified, and it should be checked for security systems and guarded by another patrol.

Forceful actions
In order to avoid any violent actions against them, the combatants take the precaution of handcuffing any crew member who resists them. They use thick plastic cuffs and imprison them inside cabins guarded by soldiers.

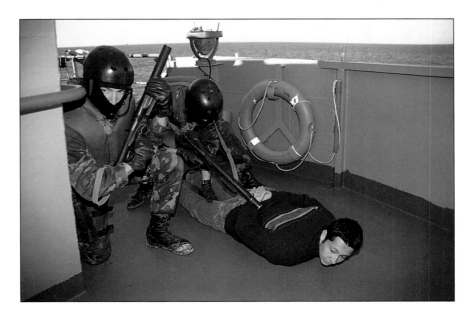

COMBAT DIVERS

The nations of Europe maintain in their military organizations, especially within the navy, groups specialized in carrying out military activities in the water: these men are combat divers. They are qualified in diving as a maneuvering technique and are specialists in accomplishing a variety of missions. These include cooperating with aquatic operations by carrying out reconnaissance on the beach prior to the deployment of troops, destroying obstacles that interfere with naval movements, attacking enemy ships, engaging in intelligence tasks, destroying or neutralizing coastal installations or equipment, experimenting with new operational techniques and evaluating new methods or special materials.

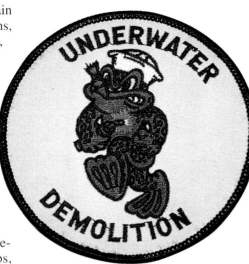

Combative
Training, operational qualifications and equipment are vital to the success of diving missions.

Commander Gorordo

The Spanish Navy maintains active a special combat divers unit, the Unidad Especial de Buceadores de Combate (UEBC), which is based at the La Algameca naval station on the outskirts of Cartagena. It is composed of fifty professionals qualified by the navy's diving center, Centro de Buceo de la Armada (CBA), with many years of experience in diving.

Special missions

The men of the UEBC are responsible for various missions under the category of special navy warfare, Guerra Naval Especial (GNE), which includes missions against strategic and operational targets that require special actions and can't be carried out by other naval forces. They are also in charge of special

reconnaissance and direct actions. These types of activities include reconnaissance for other forces, obtaining and communicating vital intelligence information, locating and patrolling enemy installations, capturing targets of special importance, hydrographic reconnaissance prior to assaults by water and reconnaissance after attacks to observe the damage suffered.

These missions require the use of various types of special equipment and continuous training with similar units from other countries. Units are deployed from ground units or submarines or use helicopters and planes for parachute jumps like HAHO (High Altitude High Opening) and HALO (High Altitude Low Opening) manual jumps with oxygen tanks. They also use small

Great capacity
Specialized divers can carry out their missions during the day or at night and under any atmospheric conditions. In fact, they use these adverse conditions to gain control of the enemy.

Equipment
To carry out the activities inherent to maneuvers on the surface and under the water, it is necessary to use complex and expensive equipment.

surface vessels or four-wheel-drive vehicles to move around.

UEBC units have many types of equipment available to them: compressed air tanks which are demagnetized to avoid activating any mines in the area, closed circuit oxygen tanks that don't emit bubbles that could alert their presence to the enemy, Harris modem terminals for sending information and photos quickly via communications links, AN/PVS-7C night vision systems that can be used underwater and

sophisticated GPS (Global Position Systems) that work in P code. In addition, they are provided with MILA mines capable of neutralizing any ship, Star Z-84 automatic rifles with the front end of the barrel coiled up, a silencer and a laser illuminator for aiming, Star 30M sturdy pistols and C-75 7.62x51 mm high precision rifles and M60 medium machine guns that are attached to revolving stands in the prow of the pneumatic vessels used during assaults.

The members of the Portuguese Navy's sapper detachment, Destacamento de Merghulladores Sapadores (DMS), are very similar to the UEBC units. They are based near Lisbon and divided into two DMS of about twenty men each. These specialists dominate all the

diving techniques and are qualified in all the specialties possible in Portugal, and their training includes a special qualification course in diving with closed circuit tanks.

Other Portuguese specialists are the divers of the special actions unit, Destacamento de Acciones Especiales (DAE), which use compressed air and closed circuit oxygen tanks. This small unit has recently received more powerful armaments such as MP5 automatic rifles, Glock pistols and Mossberg Mariner shotguns. These weapons enable them to carry out amphibious assaults, sabotage, reconnaissance and destruction of targets.

Excellent reputation

Another group with a high level of operational qualification is the British Special Boat Service (SBS), considered among military circles worldwide as one of the best because of the professionalism of its mem-

GERMAN MP5SD6 AUTOMATIC RIFLE

Commando missions require the use of light arms that are powerful, but discreet to use. One of the most effective weapons of this type is the Heckler und Köck automatic rifle or machine gun pistol. It has a retractable metallic butt that folds into the interior of the weapon and can be pulled out for those situations when it is necessary to aim accurately. It also has a silencer attached to the barrel that can reduce the sonic bang associated with the firing of its 9x19 mm Parabellum cartridges.

In addition, the weapon has a selector with four positions: safety, shot to shot, controlled burst of three cartridges and uncontrolled burst. It weighs 7.5 pounds, measures only 24 inches with the butt folded in and has a shortened barrel of only 5.7 inches. It can fire up to 800 shots per minute and the speed of the bullet leaving the barrel is about 935 feet per second. Using subsonic munitions like this greatly reduces the firing noise of this weapon.

Deployment
Pneumatic launches, like this one transporting members of the Spanish UEBC, allow for the rapid and safe transportation of combat divers to the point where they will begin their mission.

bers and their rate of success in past missions. These missions have included participation in the war in the Falkland Islands during which, following a long plane flight, they parachuted into the water and were picked up by a submarine that brought them to the coast of the archipelago. They also operated on the coast of Argentina to pass intelligence information to the command center.

The SBS is assigned to the Royal Marines, and the Director of Special Forces (DSF) controls the most reputable special units. His men follow a rigorous selection and training process and carry out exercises in various parts of the world like Scotland, Brunei and Norway. They are instructed in maneuvering a vessel and practice insertion by diving techniques.

Within the same unit are the M squadron, which is specialized in counter terrorist naval actions, and the C squadron, which groups together specialists trained in maneuvering surface vessels and the modern mini-submarines purchased from the U.S. in 1999. Their armaments are very modern and include SIG P229 pistols, Smith & Wesson

.357 Magnum revolvers, Accuracy International and Parker Hale high precision rifles, M16A2 assault rifles and M60 machine guns.

Naval combat
One of the missions entrusted to combat divers is to approach enemy docks and attach explosives under the keels of vessels or capture important enemy personnel.

Powerful launches
The use of semi-rigid pneumatic launches powered by powerful motors guarantees excellent tactical mobility in the zone of action. These vessels can be transported by navy surface craft or launched from transport planes.

Italy is home to the Commando Subacquei ed Incu (COMSUBIN) unit with its Varignano naval base near La Spézia. These divers have inherited the fame enjoyed by Prince Borghese's combat divers during the Second World War. They are specialized in sabotage, attacking naval targets or those near the coast, mining operations, guarding navy installations and Italian ships, collaborating in rescue missions and combating terrorist forces.

The COMSUBIN is organized into the Gruppo Operativo Incursore (GOI), the Gruppo Operativo Subacquei (GOS), and the Gruppo Navale Speciale (GNS). The first two are combat groups and the third provides logistical support and technical assistance. The close to

Anti-terrorist capacity
The members of the dutch 7 NC SBS (special boat squadron) unit are qualified for underwater intervention and to assault objectives both on the coast and on oil rigs.

300 naval specialists integrated in the *commando* participate in an initial selection process followed by a 10 month training course in special operations, parachuting, demolitions, armaments, hand to hand combat and diving. The members of the GOI go through an additional 42 weeks of training.

The equipment available to these groups is very advanced and ranges from mini-submarines with room for two passengers to Heckler und Köck P11 underwater pistols which can fire five small spears for neutralizing targets deep down or on the surface of the water. Their arsenal also includes tactical vests, combat uniforms and diving suits, rappelling harnesses, MP5 automatic rifles with

Specific equipment
To carry out activities in the water, it is necessary to have equipment such as wetsuits, flippers, masks, gloves, weights, compressed air tanks and vests.

viewfinders and spotlight, Beretta M92SB 9x19 mm pistols and berets which identify them as members of that special unit.

Specialized in diving
Other groups are active in various countries. As part of the Forvarskommando Nord unit of the Norwegian Navy, there is a group specialized in deep sea diving to carry out reconnaissance missions or sabotage enemy naval installations.

Marinejägers
This is the name of these Norwegian divers who train on a frequent basis with the U.S. Navy SEALs. More than 100 men are based at the Ramsund Naval Station in Nordland.

Their unique training requires an initial course of 22 weeks at the

Dykkerog Froskemannsskolen school at the Haakonsvern naval station on the outskirts of Bergen. Here, they receive training in the art of underwater deployments and maneuvering all types of vessels. Then they move to the naval base at Ramsund where they complete their training in the main methods of insertion –closed circuit tanks, canoes and parachuting– and in the use of explosives and weapons like MP5 automatic rifles, H&K pistols and assault rifles, Carl Gustav 84 mm grenade launchers and NM-142 7.62 mm precision rifles.

Denmark is home to the Fromandskorpset with its base at the Kongsore naval station in Zealand. Their armaments include G41 5.56 assault rifles, H&K 13E machine guns, Remington Wingmaster model 870 shotguns, Smith & Wesson special .38 revolvers and Mp53 and MP5SD automatic rifles. Their

Coastal target
Men specialized in combat actions on enemy coasts should be familiar with other techniques for maneuvering in this difficult area and successfully completing their mission

Mines
One of the basic missions of specialists in combat diving is to approach enemy ships and attach mines to their hulls to neutralize them. During these actions, the divers use breathing equipment that does not emit bubbles and is demagnetized

mission is to infiltrate zones that Navy ships can't reach (coastal zones, fiords and harbor installations), to attack ships, carry out special reconnaissance, sabotage enemy installations and engage in combat during direct actions.

They were formed in 1957 under the authority of the Danish diving school, and since 1970, they have been part of the SOK general headquarters. During peacetime, they assist the police in searching for people and carry out underwater demolitions and difficult diving operations.

CLOSED CIRCUIT EQUIPMENT

Several companies from various countries have manufactured sophisticated closed circuit diving equipment like the Fenzy PO-68 and the Dragüer LAR V, VI and VII. They are basically composed of a synthetic metal framework, chosen because it is demagnetized to avoid detonating active mines, which is attached to the diver's chest to facilitate his movements in depths of up to 25 or 30 feet.

On the upper part of the framework there are tubes which are attached to the mouthpiece that allows the diver to breathe. The middle section has a filter, normally made of welded lime, which neutralizes any remnants of gas expelled during breathing. At the bottom, there is a small tank with pressurized liquid oxygen for breathing underwater. The advantage of this system is that it doesn't emit bubbles to the surface which could alert the diver's presence to the enemy. However, it can only be used in depths up to 30 feet and requires previous training to use.

Recent actions in wartime have included deployments on Danish ships fighting in the Gulf War to assist in protecting the ships while at port or on the open seas and to board intercepted vessels.

The unit is composed of fifty people divided into teams of six men each, including one soldier specialized in counter terrorist naval actions to protect Danish petroleum interests in the North Sea. In addition, they often collaborate with their Swedish counterparts, the Kurstjaegerskolan.

The Dutch also have a special group of divers, called the 7 NL SB, whose members come from the Paratroopers Marine Corps. These naval commandos regularly train with highly qualified units worldwide and maintain a group specialized in assaulting passenger ships in case of a hijacking. They are specialists in diving with closed circuit tanks and are trained in tactical swimming and jungle and desert combat. They can also use explosives and take tactical photographs from any beach.

The Irish experience

Ireland maintains active a group of Rangers known as Sciathán Fianóglach an Airm descended from the traditions of the legendary Irish warriors. It is composed of soldiers from the army, navy and air force who participate in training in the tactics of small units, physical strengthening, weapons use and individual military targets.

Their many missions include carrying out deep reconnaissance patrols and VIP security, freeing hostages and counter terrorism activities. They are also prepared to engage in conventional war or support civilian authorities. During the training process, some specialize in combat diving, which requires a preliminary diving course of two weeks under the supervision of specialists from the Army Ranger Wing (ARW). This course allows them to gain con-

fidence in underwater deployments before participating in the next phase at the Naval Service Diving Section.

The second phase takes three weeks and includes reconnaissance of the hull of a ship, underwater navigation, decompressing and maneuvering small vessels and improving personal skills. During an additional phase of seven days the students carry out reconnaissance on beaches and coastal areas, board ships and learn combat techniques that they will demonstrate during a final exercise in the North Sea. For this simulation, they use Steyr AUG assault rifles with shortened barrels, aiming viewfinders and Beta-Mag clips with room for 100 cartridges.

The Mediterranean Sea is a very different combat area. It is home to the Omada Ymourthon Katastpofon

Equipped for the job
In order to maneuver, communicate and breathe in especially difficult waters and complete their mission, it is necessary for divers to use complex equipment.

Collaboration
Submarines are an excellent way of transporting small units of divers to a point near the enemy coast. Then pneumatic vessels are used to covertly transport trios of men to the shore.

(OYK), members of the combat divers unit that patrol the coastal area and multiple islands adjacent to the Greek mainland. They are divided into small groups of specialists, normally one to four men with an OYK available for training when necessary, based on the configuration of the U.S Navy SEALs teams. This facilitates their deployment for carrying out exercises or training in deactivating mines, under-water demolitions, reconnaissance and preparation of beaches, infiltration, sabotage and assaulting ships.

In addition to their highly professional training, their excellent physical condition allows them to dive without needing a rest, jump into the water from high speed boats and complete an obstacle course with heights up to 110 feet. The training process is completed with a course in

parachuting or with real deployments, such as the Gulf War during which they boarded 217 ship to enforce the embargo against Iraq.

Squaramaga is home to the divers unit known as Monas Ymourhon Katastpofon (MYK), a group of one hundred men with use of the most modern equipment: closed circuit diving tanks, camouflage uniforms similar to the U.S tiger stripes, AR-15A2 assault rifles with retractable butt and shortened barrel, M16 rifles with M203 40 mm single-shot grenade launchers, disposable rocket launchers, MG-3 medium machine guns, P11 pistols that shoot small spears and Ingram and MP5 automatic rifles with silencers. They also have mini-submarines which can be attached to the hull of submarines to be transported to the area of activity.

The different European countries maintain various groups of commandos organized under the control of the army, navy or air force. These groups can perform various mission designated as special for their level of difficulty or the complex operational requirements they demand.

In general, these units are composed of small groups of personnel with a wide range of professional experience who devote many years of service to special missions. They participate in unique and continuous training, are provided with special equipment and materials and are deployed, during exercises or real interventions, in a discreet manner so as not to alert the military forces of other countries.

Excellent reputation

The missions carried out by the British Special Air Service (SAS) have earned them an excellent reputation and recognition as one of the

Prepared for action

Paratrooper units include patrols specialized in deep reconnaissance and infiltrating enemy lines to prepare parachute landing zones. These men must be better trained and more qualified than their fellow paratroopers.

elite forces worldwide. These mission were successfully completed during the Second World War and afterwards in Malaysia, Borneo,

Oman, the Falklands, Ulster, Zaire, Bosnia and the Persian Gulf, where they were responsible for locating Iraqi Scud ground to ground missile launchers. In addition, they com-

Missions in the water

Training of these specialists includes familiarization with aquatic environments in case they must maneuver and combat in them. Therefore, they train in diving, swimming and surface navigation.

The members of the Italian battalion, Col. Moshin, are a very qualified commando force. They demonstrate their capacities every two years during the international tests of special operations patrols in Jaca, Spain.

pleted a spectacular rescue mission in May 1980 of 26 people held hostage in the Iranian embassy in London.

Many years of activity

The SAS, under the command of the British Army, was born out of the firm belief of Captain David Stirling that small groups of well-trained men could carry out sabotage actions after using various techniques to infiltrate enemy lines. Currently, active units include the 22nd Regiment in Hereford (in rotation with a group on the Credenhill Air Force Base) and the 21st and 23rd Reserve Regiments with bases in London and Birmingham. The 63rd SAS Signal Squadron works as a support force in the area of communications.

The selection process is very tough, including a final march of 95

miles over the Brecon beacons weighed down with a heavy pack; some men have died during the test. Only 10 % of those initially selected are actually accepted for further training which includes parachuting, Close Quarter Battle (CBQ) tactics, firing all types of weapons, operating communications systems and first aid. Combat exercises take place at the Jungle Warfare School in Belize, deep reconnaissance in Germany and simulations in the extreme cold in Norway and Scotland.

Their personal equipment varies

depending on their military or security mission. In addition, they change clothes depending on the area so that they are always perfectly concealed during their mission. A knowledge of foreign languages also helps with this task. The assigned equipment includes everything necessary for parachuting, maneuvering over all types of terrain, deployments in the water and diving. Important armaments include Sig Sauer P226 pistols, various models of the H&K MP5 automatic rifle, Colt M16 rifles with M203 single-shot grenade launchers and H&K G3 assault rifles with .308 Winchester cartridges.

Similar situations

Ireland has integrated a Ranger unit called the Sciathan Fhiannoglaigh an Airmin into its defense forces. An initial selection

Constant training

The Belgian Para-Commando Brigade is a unit of close to 3,000 men trained in special techniques, including small groups better trained in guerrilla and anti-guerrilla tactics.

Observation of targets

The specialists in special operations should be qualified to observe assigned targets, evaluate their potential power and communicate the information to the command. They must also carry out reconnaissance after attacks.

phase of four weeks and an additional six months of classes and exercises provide training in shooting, first aid, the use of explosives, advanced navigation, parachuting, communications and other subjects. This qualifies the men to participate in long range patrol actions, collaborate in rescue operations and take charge of the security of relevant people and places.

Some of the members of the Army Ranger Wing (ARW), as they are also called, are specialized in HALO and HAHO manual parachute jumps and others have passed diving courses at the Naval Service Diving Section. In addition, some have attended specific naval courses and are well versed in the maneuvering of small vessels, while others have

completed a seven week training period to become select marksmen. This course includes work with H&K 33 SG/1 5.56 rifles and semi-automatic rifles and Accuracy L96A1 .308 Winchester bolt action rifles. Other weapons available to the ARW include Sig Sauer P226 pistols with powerful spotlights, Remington model 870 bolt action shotguns with 12/70 caliber, MP5 automatic rifles and Steyr AUG assault rifles.

Belgian commandos

The special situation of Belgium and the decision of its government to donate troops to NATO have led to the maintenance of various military units specialized in special actions. Training is carried out at the

British Army

Great Britain maintains various groups of special forces including the army's green berets. These professionals are deployed in all types of exercises to prepare the way for ground troops.

Commando Training Center (CTC), located 10 miles from Namur, where almost 40,000 candidates have already been selected for admittance to the Para-Commando Brigade.

The training center has four companies in charge of instruction during the initial four months and the subsequent specific courses that range from a week long camouflage class to a month and a half long select marksmen course. In addition, they provide intensive training in subjects like mountains and hand to hand combat.

Operational units

A specialized course in intelligence is run by the units of the Detachment Long Range Reconnaissance Patrols (LRRP) in Heverlee (Leuven). Its 43 members, of which one-third are specialized in UDT (Underwater Demolition Team), are recruited from all the armed forces units. Their six month training period includes work in survival, identification of military equipment, communications, use of a variety of weapons, explosives and first aid. Their main mission is to collect and transmit military intelligence during wartime operations. They can also be deployed to protect embassies, carry out CSAR (Combat Search and Rescue) or eliminate key opposition forces.

LRRP units have been deployed in Zaire, Turkey, Yugoslavia, Kosovo and various African countries to participate in peace-keeping missions, NATO missions or those that support Belgian national interests. Similar activities are carried out by the Para-Commando Brigade, which was formed in 1952 out of a union between paratrooper and commando units. Currently, it is composed of three Infantry battalions: the 1st and 3rd specialized in parachuting and the 2nd in special operations.

A part of its 3,000 members, qualified as an Immediate and Rapid Reaction Force, are trained at the Marche-les Dammes CTC, where they complete five months before

attending a course in automatic parachuting at the Schaffen Parachutist

Quality armaments
European commando units are equipped with excellent weapons including Steyr AUG 5.56x45 mm assault rifles and H&K MGS90 7.62x51 mm semiautomatic high precision rifles.

Heavy load
This Belgian Para-Commando carries an enormous backpack that will enable him to survive for several days in hostile territory. Soldiers must have excellent physical endurance to travel many miles with a load that can weigh up to 150 pounds.

Training Centre. This training, along with constant work in assaults by helicopter and operational deployments, continues at their home bases where they complete an operational specialization. They train with the help of pneumatic vessels, reconnaissance vehicles and communications equipment like INMARSAT A/C communicators and BAMS radios. They also have the use of weapons including FNC carbines, Accuracy AW high precision rifles, MAG medium machine guns and 60 and 80 mm mortars.

Jaegerkorpset
This Danish unit was organized under army control in 1961 from the

examples of the British SAS and the U.S. Rangers witnessed by the Danish officials sent to both schools to familiarize themselves with their training and techniques. Since then, it has continued developing into reconnaissance patrols, combat teams that carry out sabotage and direct actions and counter terrorist units. In addition, the "jaegers" collaborate with the police action group Aktions-Styrken.

Their own aircraft collaborate with German and British helicopters or use the Hughes 500 Cayuse helicopters of the Danish Air Force. Assigned armaments include variants of the MP5 rechambered for 9x19 mm Parabellum cartridges, the 5.56x45 mm MP5, G41 assault rifles and Heckler und Köck 13E machine guns.

The Austrain Jagdkommando and the Norwegian Haerens Jaegerkommando are similar to the Danish special forces unit in terms of function, training and operational possibilities. Norway also maintains reconnaissance units called Oppklaringseskadronen, a naval assault group known as Marinejaegerkommandoen and FSK teams in command of special defense actions.

Sweden is home to the Bassäkerhetskompaniet, a small unit specialized in neutralizing the actions of enemy forces deployed to carry out sabotage on naval bases.

Firepower support
During insertion activities, commando groups need help from their fellow soldiers who must cover them with weapons capable of providing accurate support that guarantees their safety.

They work in squadrons of four men armed with AK5 rifles and a dog for help in searching. For assistance with neutralizing potential saboteurs, they normally collaborate with the Rangers of the Norwegian Air Force, the Flygbasjägarna, or the military police, the Militärpolisjägarna.

Denmark also maintains Navy patrols, the Sledgepatrol Sirius, configured by two commanding officers and 11 dogs that work in arctic areas. Their missions last for 25 months during which they only keep in contact with their superiors by radio and regroup on a ship once each year. The harsh conditions of the terrain force them to survive by their own resources, and they confront any enemy forces with M53 bolt action rifles and Glock 20 semiautomatic pistols with 10 mm Auto caliber.

Collecting intelligence information
One of the basic missions of commando groups is infiltrating enemy lines and communicating any pertinent information to their command, an activity which requires the use of communications equipment via satellite like the Cheetah.

The special situation of Germany, which shares a border with former Eastern block countries, has led to the maintenance of a very powerful armed forces and the organization of various groups specialized in carrying out missions to halt any hypothetical attacks against Western interests. With the fall of the Berlin Wall and the reunification of the military forces of West and East Germany, many things have changed. The most significant change has been Parliament's authorization to allow soldiers to carry out certain missions outside of German territory.

Special response

These organizational and politi-

Protected advance

These men have banded together to protect, with their weapons and bulletproof shields, a group of civilians they have just rescued during a training exercise. This type of action could take place in a foreign country during a popular revolt.

Equipped

German commandos have received sophisticated combat equipment for carrying out military actions, including this black uniform for urban combat missions.

cal changes led to the creation in 1994 of a new group of special forces called the Kommando Spezial Kräfte or KSK, a unit that is projected to be fully operational by the year 2000.

Varied missions

The majority of its members come from the commando companies of the three airborne brigades and the deep reconnaissance companies which, since 1996, have been integrated into the KSK. The organization is led by a brigadier and is composed of a general communications headquarters, four commando companies, one deep reconnaissance company, one support company and a training squad.

Each commando company includes five squads —one command and four action. The action squads are composed of four teams of four soldiers each trained in the specialties of medicine, communications, explosives and group leader. One squad in each company is qualified in evacuation of civi-

CH-53 STALLION HELICOPTER

The Germans have more than a hundred Stallion model G heavy transport helicopters manufactured by VFM-Fokker with permission from the U.S. firm Sikorsky. These machines are powered by three General Electric T64 turbines with a combined horsepower of 13,000. They have a large main rotor and seven blades which allow for a very stable flight, but also give the helicopter the agility it needs to carry out its military activities.

The pilots sit in a cabin at the front with great visibility, while the passenger section takes up the largest part of the fuselage with access to the rear ramp and the side doors. The tactical advantages of this helicopter are its large radius of action, cargo capacity of fifty men or several light vehicles and high speed. It is especially useful in special missions because of its wide operational possibilities and because part of its 13 metric ton cargo capacity can be replaced by additional fuel tanks attached to the sides of the fuselage. This allows it to carry out missions of more than 1600 miles without stopping to refuel.

lians during crisis situations and rescuing hostages.

The deep reconnaissance company is composed of a command and two large radius of action squads divided into 20 teams of four men each specialized in deployments anywhere it is necessary to obtain pertinent and beneficial intelligence information. The headquarters includes only one squad, while four are responsible for maintaining communications links. In addition, one of the other four squads is associated with reconnaissance missions that operate long range systems in HF (High Frequency) and satellite links.

The support company includes members responsible for logistical tasks, maintenance of parachutes, repairs and medicine.

Unique training

In general, their missions takes place behind enemy lines or in positions of conflict. Their actions include defending the territories of Germany and other NATO nations, participating in crisis situations and supporting peace-keeping missions. These include activities such as attacking targets like enemy communications lines and headquarters, carrying out deep reconnaissance, protecting German citizens in zones of conflict, liberating hostages with the Hostage Rescue Team and rescuing pilots shot down.

Members must be in excellent physical condition and participate in constant technical preparation that begins with an intensive selection process. Those who are chosen spend three months undergoing intensive training based on U.S. Special Forces and British Special Air Service methods. During this period, the most qualified are chosen to continue training in HALO and HAHO manual parachute jumps with oxygen, combat diving and other subjects. It takes three years for the men to reach the level necessary for combat.

Their equipment is modern and includes German Infantry uniforms,

black jumpsuits with tactical boots, Nomex ski masks so they won't be recognized, Eagle belts with space for pistols and clips and Gerber Mark II knives. In addition, they have the use of lightweight communications systems with earphones and microphones for links without using any hands, automatic and manual parachutes, large backpacks for reconnaissance, and Kevlar helmets and shields for direct actions.

Basic armaments are H&K G36 5.56x45 mm assault rifles used in the standard version, the shortened K model and the heavy variant configured as a light machine gun. They also use H&K MP5SD5 9x19 mm Parabellum automatic rifles with silencers, P8 pistols with the same caliber and Accuracy L96 .300 Winchester Magnum high precision

Manual parachuting
These commandos are trained in various parachuting techniques including manual methods that allow for a more accurate and discreet landing.

Coastal actions
Members of combat divers units normally train in all types of coastal actions. This photo shows a group of commandos, equipped with MILAN anti-tank missile launchers, disembarking from a pneumatic launch.

rifles in the G22 model with retractable butt. Additional weapons include P11 pistols that fire spears underwater, H&K 21 5.56 light machine guns, H&K 23 and MG3 7.62x51 mm medium machine guns, Panzerfaust 3 rocket launchers and MILAN wire-guided missile systems. Assault rifles are normally used with laser aiming devices and powerful spotlights for firing in dimly lit areas. Unimog 2 ton trucks and Mercedes Benz G Wagen vehicles are useful for maneuvering.

Training center
Special training in large radius reconnaissance actions led to the creation of the International Long Range Reconnaissance Patrol School (ILRRPS). Since 1997, it has been located in Pfullendorf at

the Generalobert von Fritsch headquarters, south of Stuttgart and 30 miles north of Lake Contstance.

The center, led by a German colonel, has the mission of training specialists for various NATO countries. They carry out basic training and individual and patrol preparations in everything related to deep reconnaissance missions within special operations.

The center is organized into a Staff Officers Command with German personnel, two project sections and two WING groups – I is international and II is exclusively for German soldiers. The Staff

Officers Command is divided into six sections (S1 to S6), the command, the administration, medical services, training assistants and the mail office.

The WING's are composed of administrative and training sections and four divisions: reconnaissance, patrol, survival and medicine. Each division has a commanding officer and half a dozen permanent instructors. The Reconnaissance division

runs various one to two week courses including Identification of Material Training (IMT) classes: IMT for those in charge of verifying compliance with the treaty of the Conventional Forces in Europe (CFE), Specialist in IMT and IMT for countries belonging to the Community of Independent States (CIS).

The Patrol division runs training periods of up to three weeks in planning operations, basic patrolling, advanced patrolling, patrol leader and winter patrolling. The survival division teaches a course aimed at pilots during which they train for one to ten days in survival practice with emphasis on resisting interrogation. In addition, there is a two week course on close range shooting and three week courses for select marksmen or combat survival. The medicine division runs a

Rescue
One of the most interesting exercises carried out by the KSK is the rescue of civilians caught in a hostile environment. This mission requires the use of helicopters and the deployment of a considerable number of soldiers.

course for patrol medical assistants that lasts three weeks. The center is also home to the German 200 Deep Reconnaissance Company, which collaborates in general training.

Specialization in Diving

The Germans maintain a unit of combat divers, the Kampfschiwimmerkompanie (KSK), which is integrated in the navy and stationed at the Eckernförde Naval Base. Their missions include those under the control of the United Nations, reconnaissance of coastal areas and surveillance of maritime traffic, direct actions including attacks on ships in port and coastal targets, destruction of harbor installations and defense of German installations.

Their training is very selective and begins with a basic phase during which 80% of the candidates are eliminated. Basic requirements including swimming 8 miles in a

Vertical encircling
One of the rules of special operations is that they must be carried out quickly and by surprise. If these orders are followed, a successful mission without casualties is much more likely.

certain time, holding their breath for 45 seconds and swimming 80 feet underwater. A four week training period teaches basic diving skills, and later they are prepared to use closed circuit diving tanks. Finally, an eight week combat course includes parachute work, commando training and vehicle maneuvering. At the end of this training period, the soldiers should be able to stay underwater for two minutes and swim the length of a pool bottom of 250 feet.

Then they complete a specific combat divers course that includes explanations of tactical subjects, maneuvering all types of vessels, operating with helicopters, diving in the Baltic Sea in depths up to 100 feet and simulations of all types of attacks on important German Navy

ports. At the end of this physical and technical strengthening, which only 5% of the candidates complete, they should be capable of swimming underwater up to 50 miles with a 100 pound waterproof bag filled with all the necessary equipment.

The two hundred men of the Kampfschwimmer have access to equipment such as Klepper kayaks, Dräger LAR V diving tanks, MP5 automatic rifles, H&K PSG-1 semi-automatic precision rifles, Zodiac and RIB vessels and 40 mm grenade launchers. Their recent military activities have included deployments in the Persian Gulf to enforce the U.N. embargo against Iraq and deactivating mines during Operation Desert Storm.

Generously armed
Two KSK operators advance covering each other with their personal weapons including H&K P8 pistols and H&K G-36K assault rifles with aiming laser and spotlight for dark areas.